HOW TO THRIVE AS A WOMAN PHYSICIAN

FOREWORD BY
BETSY FLANAGAN, MBA

TAMMIE CHANG, MD
& LUISA DURAN, MD

Design by Marie O'Shepherd
Photography by Sophia Mavrides

For permission requests, please email the authors at
info@pinkcoatmd.com

Paperback ISBN 978-1-7378567-0-2
Ebook ISBN 978-1-7378567-1-9

TO OUR DAUGHTERS, MAY YOUR LIGHT FOREVER SHINE BRIGHTLY.

For anyone who cares about making the medical profession as equitable and as excellent as it can be, this book is essential. It should be required reading for all medical trainees and attending physicians, regardless of gender.

JENNIFER A. BARKLEY, MD
Internal Medicine/Pediatrics

Every woman in medicine and surgery should read this book! This book fills a much-needed gap (abyss is more like it) in our medical and surgical training by addressing the complexities of being a woman physician. The resources in this book are unique, well thought out, compassionate, and data driven. This will be a resource I frequently use throughout my career.

ELIZABETH BERDAN, MD, MS
Pediatric General & Thoracic Surgery

Making it through medical training is difficult, and you hope that when you start your life as an attending, things will automatically fall into place. Of course, it's not that easy, and this book is an amazing guide to help us navigate this stressful time. With each friendly and personal chapter, I felt they were supporting me through important strategies to becoming the best version of myself. This is a great quick read that gives you a lot to ponder for what I suspect to be years to come.

VANESSA TOLBERT, MD
Pediatric Hematology-Oncology

It's hard to know where to start to describe how much I have learned from and grown through my involvement with Pink Coat, MD. I learned throughout my training that you had to have support in many forms, but once I became an attending I found I still needed that support. There are new challenges and changes that take place after you make the transition, and Pink Coat, MD really gives you the tools at any stage of training to deal with our very difficult but rewarding field. Having a community of similarly experienced women of all life stages in medicine really provides the support that I feel so many would benefit from. I'm grateful and plan to keep learning and growing with this awesome group.

SARAH WALKER, MD
Pediatric Surgery

I only wish that this book had been around early in my medical career. Having practiced as an Emergency Physician in academic, government and private settings, this book speaks to me and truly reflects experiences, many of which are like mine and those of my female colleagues. Many female physicians are struggling to balance their professional, personal and family lives, and the feeling of not doing any of them well is so common! What's wonderful about this book is that it not only makes one feel they are not alone, but gives excellent advice on how to take care of oneself and avoid or manage burnout.

JOAN BURG, MD
Emergency Medicine

As physicians we are providers — for our families, friends, and patients. Yet can we provide for ourselves? Can we maintain the energy and love that led us to medicine in the first place? Reading this book empowered me with the evidence, reflective questions and action items to resoundingly say, "Yes we can!"

BONNIE LAU, MD PHD
Pediatric Hematology-Oncology

Tammie and Luisa share their personal stories, including the experiences and feelings we have all had during med school, residency, and entering practice. Following their journeys, their strength and growth, is inspirational and reaffirming. This book is a gift to all women physicians!

DANA CHORTKOFF, MD
Obstetrics-Gynecology

I thoroughly enjoyed this book; I only wish it had been available earlier in my career. Tammie and Luisa's book is a call to change a system where burnout is so prevalent that we cease to recognize it or question it. In this book I found not only validation of what I had experienced during training and as an attending but also actionable advice on how to recover from burnout and rekindle a love for medicine.

BARBARA THOMPSON, MD, MBA
Pediatric Endocrinology

CONTENTS

FOREWORD

When I met Luisa in 2016, she was an endocrinologist who felt stuck. She didn't even have a sink to wash her hands in her only exam room and had to fight tooth and nail for *years* to get it. Can you *imagine*? She felt far removed from the passion that led her to medicine. She was tired, lonely, demoralized by the system, and felt so powerless to make it better that she even considered leaving the career she had worked her whole life to achieve.

Maybe you picked up this book because you can relate.

Luisa took my "Power and Influence: Women in Leadership" class at UC Berkeley, and since then, we have worked together to clarify her values, understand her strengths, and find ways for her to shape her professional career and personal life. Our work together included breaking free from the old rules and systems that made her feel stuck and hid her true power.

In 2019, Luisa reconnected with her dear friend Tammie from medical school, and they immediately found common experiences, frustrations, and aspirations. Tammie had just come back from the lowest point in her life, having suffered from severe burnout and mental illness to the point of being suicidal. She returned after a leave of absence from her career as a pediatric hematologist/oncologist, driven and on fire to make things better for the women who were fellow physicians and colleagues. I started working with Tammie and Luisa to help launch Pink Coat, MD in 2020, a resource for women physicians to find more fulfillment in their personal and professional lives.

This is their handbook, written to help you shape your medical career and the world around you and to make it what you hoped it could be when you started your career in medicine. They are telling you, physician to physician, woman to woman: *don't give up*! You have much more power than you think. If you are tired, overwhelmed, discouraged by corporate medicine, there are steps you can take to bring your career back in line with those big, powerful hopes and dreams that propelled you all the way to and through medical school.

This book helps you build your personal roadmap to reconnect with your visions of how you want your career to be and with your power to get there. From embracing tactics and strategies for navigating our broken healthcare system, to understanding your own highest self and personal power, to connecting with your fierce and female pack, Luisa and Tammie want you to become avid explorers on a journey back to your authentic self and true calling in medicine.

I am not a physician, but what I brought to Tammie and Luisa's journey is my knowledge of old systems, old rules, and how to break free of them. My parents—both lawyers—showed me the power of agency and how to say "no" to nonsense and to others' expectations and to say "yes" to what I wanted. Both my parents were advocates and fighters who saw the world as a blank canvas that they could design as they wanted. What I learned allows me to quickly spot someone trapped in a system that they believe is immutable and unchanging, not seeing the option to shift the rules and playing field to work for them.

In college and professionally, I was surrounded by incredibly talented, hardworking, and smart people, many of whom felt unfulfilled, unseen, and unheard. Classmates and colleagues gravitated toward me for guidance and advice. I repeatedly harkened back to what my parents taught me: that one has agency and authority to shape the world. In 2010, I started my journey to coaching, through communications, into change and leadership training, and in 2013, I became a certified coach. The training formalized much of what I had been doing informally since childhood and provided me with additional skills and tools to help my clients. The past eight years of hands-on practice have been my real education, giving me the opportunity to learn from and with my clients as we identify options to shift the rules to work for them. With each client, however unique, I experienced great joy as they found new levels of freedom, success, impact, and happiness.

This dialogue from the comedy film *Clueless* sums up my upbringing and my philosophy:

Cher Horowitz:

Daddy, did you ever have a problem that you couldn't argue your way out of?

Mel Horowitz:

Tell me the problem, and we'll figure out how to argue it.

Taking this perspective, our medical system is a "problem" that requires you to do some arguing—for yourself, to save your dreams and your career, and to set yourself up to do the important work you know you were meant to do.

In my coaching practice, I have seen physicians, especially female physicians, give selflessly to patients, peers, managers and to the organizations that demand so much. I also see that it is the core skills that allowed them to excel in medical school and clinically—such as deep subject matter expertise and dedication to study and precision, especially when following protocols and procedures—that sometimes hold them back from gaining the leadership, agency, and influence they seek. These core skills are critical clinically, yet they can also inhibit the ability to draw outside the lines and to shape the world around you.

To create the world as you want it to be may require stepping outside your area of expertise (or comfort), but it won't require anything you are not 100% capable of doing. You just need to learn how and understand you have license to do it. Consider this example: have you ever felt cornered in a meeting that turned out to be about something you did not expect? Would it ever occur to you to say, "Oh, the agenda said the meeting was about updating our protocols, but it looks like it's about something else. Let's not waste anyone's time. Let's reschedule so that we can all come prepared to talk about this topic."

For many, without the type of retraining provided in this handbook, a meeting in which you feel cornered might involve frantically searching your brain and scrambling on the spot to perform the best you can under suboptimal circumstances. Instead, this handbook provides tools and additional options to expand your repertoire, including responses that give you breathing room, "untrap" you, and change the "rules" to bring forth your best self. The material in this handbook will illustrate that you are never actually stuck.

With the focus, discipline, and hard work you have already demonstrated you are capable of, this information will help you learn how to identify these new boundaries for yourself. By engaging fully with Pink Coat, MD, you will reconnect with what inspired you to get into medicine, and what you are especially gifted at and nourished by. You will also learn to recognize when it's time to follow the rules, and when it's time to shed artificial constraints to successfully navigate the "Wild West" of hospital and medical office politics and the old, dysfunctional systems that were designed by and for someone else (someone who is not you!). So, get ready to do some work. I promise the effort will bring you to a better place.

What excites me about coaching is watching women like you experience the world in this new way. The shift can come from a conversation, from breaking down an uncomfortable experience, or from mapping out a plan for how to approach an upcoming meeting or interaction. With each successful experience, your confidence, influence, power, and agency will grow, and you will internalize the awareness that you're never really stuck.

The world needs more women to take their place in leadership. Women like Luisa and Tammie. Women like you. It is an honor and privilege to play my small role in bringing more women into leadership and to help them stay there.

Betsy Flanagan, MBA

SURROUND YOURSELF ONLY WITH PEOPLE WHO ARE GOING TO TAKE YOU HIGHER.

Oprah Winfrey

INTRODUCTION

We are so excited you decided to read this book and learn from our many years of life experience as two incredibly hard-working female physicians who care deeply about our profession, our personal well-being, our families, our communities, and our collective future in medicine. This book is written especially for the early-career woman in medicine, with the intention of serving as a guide as you transition from trainee to "in charge," so that you can navigate your life in these first few critical years.

We understand how challenging this time can be, and data show that (sadly) the odds are against us. As numerous published studies indicate, the truth is that in 2021, women physicians are less likely to rise in leadership positions and more likely to suffer from burnout, to quit medicine, and to die by suicide as compared to men, women in other professions, and women in the general population.[1,2,3,4,5] This reality is significantly exacerbated by the recent COVID-19 global pandemic. We will explain more about these challenges in subsequent chapters. Our goal is to provide you with the best resources and support to beat these odds, help a friend, and keep sharing with our world your valuable gifts and skills as incredible healers.

As you'll notice, our chapters are short and sweet. Because we understand your busy life and precious time, we are giving you a quick, easy-to-read overview of the key areas we recommend you focus on, so that you can professionally and personally thrive as women physicians in today's imperfect healthcare landscape. You can read this book beginning to end or flip through for lessons that are most helpful to you. The information in this book reflects the life lessons we've learned in more than 20 years of combined clinical experience working full-time for large healthcare organizations. These include practical strategies to overcome your struggles, rise from your lowest points, and successfully manage your stressors, challenging relationships, and many responsibilities outside of work. Most importantly, these strategies helped us stay in medicine with more peace of mind and heart, so that today we continue thriving!

Our wish for our readers is to feel hopeful that you too can thrive within our imperfect healthcare systems despite the struggles, challenges, and concerns, which arise *not* because you are weak, flawed, or in any way a failure. We stress this point, because for years we thought that we were the problem or somehow defective, and so it was incredibly healing to learn that hundreds, if not thousands of other physicians, are sharing these struggles! You are not alone! We are not alone!

We are living in a time when the chronic ills of many institutions are coming to light. Know that it is normal for you to be experiencing any degree of challenge, no matter your accolades and pristine track record. It means that you are human, and that's what we most love about you! We hope that this book inspires you to act, to change the trajectory of your life toward a brighter, healthier, happier future, AND, most importantly, to stay in medicine! Our world is a better place when you are thriving as a woman physician.

We believe in the power of connection, and so we have created a safe, loving community to help neutralize the systemic difficulties beyond our individual control. We invite you to learn more about Pink Coat, MD. We've put together a wonderful team of experts, inspirational role models, and a safe, loving, supportive group of like-minded women physicians who can help you take a deeper dive into nourishing your soul, protecting yourself, and flourishing in your medical career and life.

Let's do this!

Luisa Duran, MD & Tammie Chang, MD
July 2021

CHAPTER 01

WHY READING THIS GUIDE MATTERS

THE RELATIONSHIP WITH YOURSELF IS THE MOST IMPORTANT RELATIONSHIP YOU'LL EVER HAVE.

Judith Orloff, MD

If you're reading this book, then you're probably like us, searching for more joy in your everyday lives, for renewed purpose and a better future as a woman in the healthcare profession. Congratulations on taking the first most important step in this journey: choosing to help yourself! That's half the battle. If there's one thing we wish we had done differently in our careers, it would have been asking for help earlier! We strongly believe that seeking and receiving help are both signs of strength and leadership. Thank you for modeling this for yourself and for others.

Reading this book matters to you, because it will quickly open your mind and heart to new possibilities about how to thrive, and not just survive, as the amazing woman you are! You will learn practical strategies that you can easily put into everyday practice, designed to increase your energy, joy, life satisfaction, and emotional well-being. You will also grow more confident about having a long-term career in medicine, one that brings greater prosperity, financial wellness, power, influence, flexibility, and freedom. We've experienced all these benefits since deciding to give these strategies a try BEFORE quitting our physician jobs! Now, not only did we stay in practice, but we've also helped countless other women physicians minimize their own pains and struggles. Together we are on a path of more joy, of more career and life fulfillment, and we want this for everyone!

In the next few chapters, we will share what we learned over our years of navigating the real-life challenges of practicing medicine as two hardworking, Ivy-League-educated women physicians who were struggling in silence.

Our wish for you is to feel a little more inspired and hopeful that change is coming, because you are that change—and together, we are that change! And yes, no matter what, you too can thrive as a woman physician and love your life in medicine again!

CHAPTER 02

THE PHYSICIANS' BROKEN DREAM

YOU ARE A BRILLIANT STAR, AND WE NEED YOUR LIGHT TO HEAL THE DARKNESS.

Luisa Duran, MD

Why are we devoting our precious time and energy to writing this book? Because we refuse to settle for a broken dream!

When we were kids, we felt called to become physicians, and as mature high school seniors we acted on this calling, committing to Brown University's prestigious eight-year program in Liberal Medical Education, which held the promise that we could become world-class physicians. Since we were 18 years old, we have dedicated our lives to a path where for more than half our lifetimes, we worked incredibly hard, made tremendous sacrifices, and remained laser-focused on becoming the best physicians and on always being in service to others and our communities.

While pursuing our physician dreams, we were heartbroken to discover, at the end of our rainbow, not the happy, purpose-filled life we wanted but early years of high stress, new anxiety, unrealistic workloads, isolation, emotional exhaustion, chronic fatigue, and a lack of support to help us cope with these negative feelings and experiences as attending physicians. No one we worked with was open or knowledgeable enough to tell us that what we were experiencing at the time was physician burnout; even more alarming to us was the truth we are not on a level playing field, and that physician burnout and physician suicide are common, documented experiences among healthcare professionals, especially women physicians![6] As we'll show, this phenomenon is systemic, related to factors that disproportionately affect women in healthcare.

We were shocked to find that our path to becoming physicians was more hazardous to our health and our life than we could ever imagine, and the main toxin is our system. Contrary to our self-blame, physician burnout happens because of our jobs, NOT because we aren't resilient "enough." The truth is that 80% of physician burnout is triggered by systemic factors—that is our work environments (excessive workloads, frequent overnight call, long work hours, high work intensity), organizational culture, and professional culture.[7] And even physicians with the highest possible resiliency scores, STILL get burned out![8] As we see it: if we are practicing medicine in today's health care environment it's not a matter of IF we will burnout, it's a matter of WHEN and HOW severely.

And guess what? Being born female places us at higher risk! As women physicians we are up to a 60% higher risk of burnout compared to men.[9] Sixty percent! If this were not bad enough, we are also at MUCH higher risk of dying by suicide! O.M.G.!! Did you know that it's been known since at least 2004 that **female physicians are more than twice as likely to die by suicide compared to females in the general population?** Just think about that for a second. One study more precisely defined our suicide rate as 2.27 times greater than the general female population.[10] Another as 250-400% higher risk of dying by suicide compared to other women![11] Consider this: people living with diabetes areat a two to four times higher risk of dying by heart disease compared to people without diabetes.[12] And guess what we do as a society to help them protect against heart disease: we treat their diabetes. Why can't we as women physicians get the same preventive care?

Oh, and by the way, women in medicine are also at higher risk of sexual harassment, biases, prejudice, and discrimination. The majority of women physicians—70%—report experiencing discrimination in the workplace.[13] These negative workplace experiences are also recognized as contributors to burnout.

ARE YOU AFFECTED BY BURNOUT?[14]

01. Have you become cynical or critical at work?

02. Do you drag yourself to work and have trouble getting started?

03. Have you become irritable or impatient with staff, co-workers, colleagues, or patients?

04. Do you lack the energy to be consistently productive?

05. Do you find it hard to concentrate?

06. Do you lack satisfaction from your achievements?

07. Do you feel disillusioned about your job?

08. Are you using food, drugs, or alcohol to feel better or to simply not feel?

09. Have your sleep habits changed?

10. Are you troubled by unexplained headaches, stomach or bowel problems, or other physical complaints?

If you answered "yes" to any of these questions, you might be experiencing burnout.

In addition to these health and life hazards, we discovered that, due to gender-related factors, we are more likely to have less fulfilling careers in medicine. In fact, we are more likely to have shorter careers, limited leadership opportunities, and lower pay.

Did you know, for instance, that female physicians are more likely to leave medicine soon after completing their residencies? In 2019, the Association of American Medical Colleges published data indicating that 40% of women physicians go part-time or leave medicine altogether within six years of completing their residencies.[15] Although more than *50%* of medical school classes are now women,[16] only *34%* of the physician workforce is women.[17] That's a net loss of 16% of highly-trained women physicians who do not continue to provide services to the community. Women are also less likely to hold leadership positions.

In 2018, the *Harvard Business Review* reminded us that only 18% of deans and department chairs are women, and only 16% of hospital C-suite leaders are women.[18] To top things off, women physicians get paid significantly less than men. Medscape's *2019 Physician Compensation Report* found that full-time women (primary care and specialist physicians) earn 25-33% less than their respective male counterparts.[19]

IT IS ALSO ESTIMATED THAT, IN 2020, MALE PHYSICIANS EARNED $116,000 MORE PER YEAR THAN THEIR FEMALE COLLEAGUES[20]

Are things getting any better today? Unfortunately, the answer is "no." In fact, another reason for writing this book now is that we are facing a healthcare emergency, exacerbated by the COVID-19 global pandemic. As physicians practicing in 2021, we are seeing how the pandemic is hurting working women even more than men. According to LeanIn.org and McKinsey & Company's *Women in the Workplace* report (released September 2021), one-in-four women are contemplating downshifting their careers or leaving the workforce.[21] Women, especially women of color, are also more likely to have been laid off or furloughed during the COVID-19 crisis. All told, more than two million women have left the workforce since the pandemic began in March 2020.[22]

The number of women in the workplace is now equivalent to that of the 1980's! Since the start of the pandemic, one-in-four working mothers of children under the age of eighteen have reduced their hours in order to care for their children and family members. That compares to only one-in-six working fathers and one-in-ten working non-parents.[23]

How did the pandemic affect men? Less severely than it affected women. A study conducted in July 2020 by Qualtrics and TheBoardlist involving 1,051 salaried U.S. employees found

SAY *WHAT?!*

that men were more than *three times* as likely as women to be promoted at work since the prior year. Working fathers of children under the age of 18 were five *times* more likely to be promoted than working mothers.[24]

What does all of this mean for the future of healthcare? If these trends hold, it means a less equal, less diverse, less inclusive healthcare workforce, and most alarming, not enough physicians to take care of all of us! The physician shortage in the United States is expected to reach more than 139,000 by 2033.[25] The COVID-19 pandemic, which struck after the projections were completed, only magnifies the need to address this shortage. This is a serious and costly problem, as the expense to replace one physician can range $500,000 to more than $1 million per physician.[26] Physician burnout alone is estimated to cost the healthcare industry between $2.6 to $6.3 billion each year![27] How much more money does this dilemma need to cost us before we start making major systemic changes?

Furthermore, for individual practitioners, the dream of becoming vibrant, joyful, brilliant physicians was broken by the reality that our medical profession is often filled with darkness and silence in the face of these issues. We personally discovered a harsh medical culture filled with unhealthy competition, unrealistic expectations, impossible standards, inflexible work schedules, criticism, cynicism, negativity, implicit gender and maternal bias, sexual harassment, prejudice, discrimination, and a broken employment system with limited support for frontline workers. This toxic culture is causing women physicians in particular to miss out on fulfilling the beautiful career ideal that we have *all* worked so hard and sacrificed so much to achieve. In addition, this toxic culture, we believe, is the primary reason why nearly 70% of physicians do not want their children to become physicians.[28]

WHAT IS BURNOUT? [29]

- Emotional Exhaustion
  - Physical, mental, emotional exhaustion
- Depersonalization
  - Cynicism, sarcasm, negativity
  - Compassion fatigue
- Lack of personal accomplishment
  - Work feels meaningless
  - No sense of purpose

INDIVIDUAL RISK FACTORS OF BURNOUT[30]

- You identify so strongly with work that that your personal life suffers.
- You have a high workload, including overtime.
- You try to be everything to everyone.
- You work in a helping profession, such as healthcare.

- You feel you have little or no control over your work.
- Your job is monotonous, without purpose.

CONSEQUENCES OF BURNOUT[31]

- Excessive stress
- Fatigue
- Insomnia
- Sadness, anger, irritability
- Alcohol or substance misuse
- Heart disease
- High blood pressure
- Type 2 diabetes
- Vulnerability to illnesses

As two women physicians who have just entered our forties and are hitting our professional stride, we can see first-hand the "leaky bucket" that is our healthcare system. We are observing all these gloomy statistics in real life. We are witnessing our brilliant, incredibly talented colleagues, who take exceptional care of the most complicated patients, leave their practice of medicine for other non-medical pursuits. We are even seeing our beautiful, unbelievably gifted physician colleagues die of suicide. Just this past year we met with Corey Feist and felt the tragic loss of his sister-in-law Dr. Lorna Breen, a phenomenal emergency medicine physician who died by suicide during this unforeseen COVID-19 pandemic.

We are deeply disturbed that this truth about physician suicide has been well-documented in the literature since 2004, yet no one on our path brought it to our awareness or warned us about this potential fate. Instead, we followed blindly as physicians without knowing how risky it would be to our mental and emotional well-being. Even more troubling is the current lack of help and support for physicians experiencing mental health challenges.

We strongly believe that physicians should not have to face any repercussions for disclosing mental health assistance to licensing boards or health care institutions. It is not acceptable for us to feel afraid when we need help! The stigma and paralysis surrounding mental health created by our institutions needs to stop.

DEAR LICENSING BOARDS AND HEALTH CARE INSTITUTIONS:

> **HOW DO YOU EXPECT US TO HELP THE ESTIMATED ONE-IN-FOUR U.S. ADULTS SUFFERING FROM MENTAL ILLNESS WHEN YOU DO NOT SUPPORT US IN HELPING OURSELVES?**

ALARMING DATA ABOUT 21ST CENTURY HEALTHCARE THAT WE WANT YOU TO KNOW

- More than 50% of medical school students are women (2020).

Yet, women physicians ...

- Have 60% increased odds of burnout compared to men.
- Have a 400% higher risk of dying by suicide than women in the general population.
- 40% of those women physicians go part-time or quit medicine altogether within six years of completing their residency training.
- 70% report experiencing discrimination in the workplace.
- Earn 25–30% LESS than their male counterparts.
- Earn $116,000 LESS annually compared to male physicians (2020).

And ...

- Only 18% of deans and department chairs are women.

- Only 16% of hospital C-suite Leaders are women.

Also good to know:

- 70% of physicians do not want their children to become physicians!

- Shortage of 139,000 physicians anticipated in the United States in 2033.

- $500,000 to more than $1 million is the estimated cost of replacing one physician.

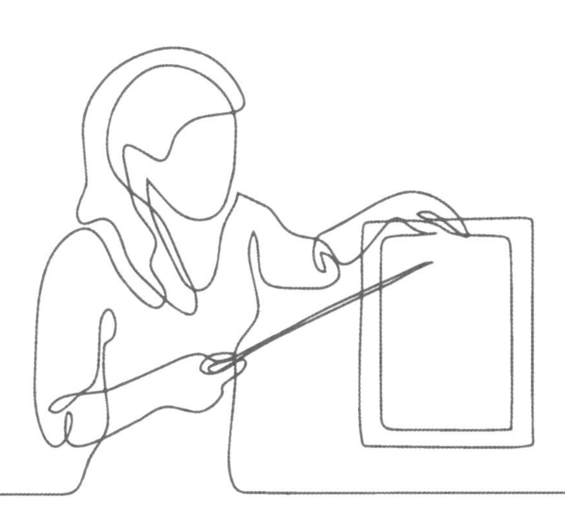

We all need to agree this makes absolutely no sense. We must join prominent Olympic phenoms like Michael Phelps, Simone Biles, and other prominent celebrities and world leaders advocating mental health support for all. Together, we can end this culture of silence, especially in healthcare.

We are now on a mission to help everyone understand this grim reality, because we've learned that by knowing the risks and occupational hazards, we can be better prepared to beat the odds of burnout and suicide and to protect our minds and hearts, ourselves, our families, our children, and our future. Isn't that what we do for our patients? We educate them about their risk for disease, and thereby empower them to take safe action and protect them from serious health injuries and deadly outcomes. Let's ask how we can do the same for ourselves and for each other.

We care deeply about our profession and about creating a brighter, healthier future in medicine for all of us, as well as for all the little girls who aspire to become physicians. We know this book will not have all the answers; still, we hope that the next few chapters will provide a glimmer of hope that you can create the life in medicine that you deserve, and that you can continue shining as the bright stars we know you are!

KEY MESSAGES

The experience for women physicians in 2021 is not equal to that of men due to higher risks for physician burnout, physician suicide, discrimination, gender biases, pay gaps, and limited opportunities for leadership. Therefore, we need resources specifically for women physicians to addresses these inequities.

Being a woman physician puts you at a higher risk for physician burnout and for physician suicide. And it's not just you—we are all at risk! We conclude from the numerous published studies about physician burnout that it's not a question of if we will burnout, it's a question of *when* and *how severely*.

Are you having any signs or symptoms of physician burnout? Please see the '*What is Burnout?*' table on page 33 to learn more.

The medical profession needs to focus on strategies to help us beat these odds. A projected physician shortage of 139,000 physicians by 2033 means that we will need *every* physician practicing today.

CHAPTER 03

PRACTICAL RESOURCES AND LIFE STRATEGIES TO COPE WITH HEALTHCARE'S IMPERFECTIONS

ASKING FOR HELP IS ALWAYS A SIGN OF STRENGTH.

Michelle Obama

Over the years, we discovered important tools that helped us:

1. to cope with the stresses of our broken healthcare system, and
2. to quickly recover from and to protect against physician burnout.

We believe that these resources and life strategies are fundamental to our success as practicing physicians. In this chapter, we want to share these resources and strategies with you, because we did not learn about these tools in our medical training, and we found tremendous benefits when incorporating these strategies into our daily lives and clinical practice.

HELPFUL PROFESSIONAL RESOURCES

These are the professional resources we have personally found most beneficial to our life and career:

- Professional coaching
- Leadership development
- Negotiation training
- Mindful self-compassion
- Parenting and family life support
- Peer support

Here we briefly review the benefits of each of these resources and how our lives have improved because we gave them a try.

1. Professional Coaching

Real-world experience has taught us that practicing as a physician takes more than knowing clinical medicine. You must also know how to navigate corporate healthcare, build skills to influence organizational systems that affect your well-being, and have confidence in your work choices and the direction of your career. You also need to enhance self-awareness, draw on individual strengths, question self-defeating thoughts and beliefs, examine new perspectives, and align personal values with professional duties. Professional coaches have the specific expertise to help physicians in this way. Partnering with a professional coach, either one-to-one or in a small group, can provide confidential, expert support to successfully navigate the workplace and life.

Evidence that professional coaching works. Scientific evidence supports the benefits of professional coaching for physicians. Physicians who receive professional coaching have a significant reduction in emotional exhaustion and overall symptoms of burnout, as well as improvements in overall quality of life and resilience. In 2019, the *Journal of American Medical Association* (JAMA) published the results of a randomized clinical trial involving 88 practicing physicians in departments of medicine, family medicine, and pediatrics who had volunteered for coaching. After six months of professional coaching, emotional exhaustion significantly decreased by 19.5% for those who received coaching versus *increasing* by 9.8% in the control group. The prevalence of symptoms of burnout significantly decreased by 17% in the physicians who received coaching and increased by 4.9% in the control group (those not receiving coaching). Also seen was a 20.3% (versus 1.5%) statistically significant improvement in overall quality of life compared with the control group, along with an increase in resilience.[32]

Notable benefits of professional coaching. In addition to these trends, discrete benefits of coaching include:

- Less emotional exhaustion
- Fewer overall symptoms of burnout
- Improvement in overall quality of life
- Increased resilience
- Opportunities for safe self-discovery and self-reflection
- A greater sense of personal agency

These benefits are reported by coaching recipients in general. Next, we'll discuss how each of us personally experienced coaching.

How we personally benefitted from professional coaching. We started working with a professional coach shortly after entering real-world medical practice. We experienced hardships like working under high productivity demands without necessary resources, convincing administrators to invest in these needed resources, managing conflict with difficult colleagues, working under terrible leadership, dealing with problematic office staff, and sometimes working in a toxic office culture, including navigating office politics, coping with poor management, and overcoming gender bias. We turned to professional coaching because our formal medical training did not provide the tools to manage these complexities.

Our coach was invaluable to our lives and careers in many ways. First, she was easy to talk to and empathic, just like the best friend we all need. Second, she was incredibly skilled at helping us strategize solutions to the clinical struggles that were rooted in complex business and organizational problems. Third, with her guidance we gained clarity on our personal strengths and core values, and we addressed limiting beliefs that were blocking our full potential. Ultimately, she empowered us to make positive changes in our work and in daily life that helped us to improve our work environments and personal lives.

We now feel more capable of creating positive change, and most importantly, we feel more in control of our lives! We invite you to try out a professional coach, and we share our recommendations for excellent professional coaching on our website at PinkCoatMD.com.

2. Leadership Development

More and more data continue to emerge that prove women make incredible leaders. Yet so many of us women physicians do not see our own leadership potential or even realize that we already *are* leaders. We have discovered that by investing in our leadership development we are able to thrive as women physicians and leaders, regardless of our title or position.

Evidence that women make excellent leaders. Especially in the wake of the COVID-19 pandemic crisis, women emerged as the better leaders, based on multiple outcome measures. Countries led by women, for example, had fewer COVID-related cases and deaths, and in the U.S., states led by a female governor had lower fatality rates.[33,34,35] Multiple studies showed that women are seen as more qualified to lead in a crisis and have higher levels of engagement with followers. In study after study, women leaders are also shown to have superior interpersonal skills, including powerful communication; greater collaboration, teamwork, higher relationship building skills; and higher overall success with inspiring and motivating others. Finally, women leaders consistently scored higher on key leadership capabilities, including taking initiative, higher resilience, driving for results, displaying integrity and honesty, developing others, and being champions of change and innovation.[36]

Notable benefits of leadership development. Intentional leadership development helps women to recognize their own leadership potential and capabilities. As physicians, we are by default the leaders of our teams, and yet we receive little to no leadership development during our medical training. What does it take to be a good leader? And what is good leadership? Ask a room of 100 leadership development experts, and you will get 100 different answers.

When we finally realize that **we are leaders now**, that we have influence now from wherever we are in an organization or institution, and that we can lead right from where we are, then we can step into our true power as women and as physicians. We can lead vertically, horizontally, and from right where we are.

HOW I PERSONALLY BENEFITTED FROM LEADERSHIP DEVELOPMENT

Tammie's Story

I was so lucky to have been introduced to the concept of leadership as a rising sophomore at Brown University. As a participant in the Brown Outdoor Leadership Training (BOLT) program, my experience as a participant had such an impact that I then became a BOLT Leader and later a Leader Trainer, teaching other new leaders how to facilitate, listen, mediate conflict, and empower others to lead. I continued to help with BOLT basecamp through my time in the medical school at Brown.

So, it's with this foundation in leadership that I entered the next several years of residency and fellowship, where I did not see the same kind of servant leadership modeled around me. It was not until five years into practice following medical training that I began to study, read, and explore what leadership could be. I felt a deep longing for a different kind of leadership than what I had seen modeled for so many years.

I became a leadership junkie, reading every leadership book I could find and attending numerous leadership courses and programs. I became a certified leadership coach, taught leadership courses, and created a women's physician attending leadership development program for the American Medical Women's Association. Most importantly, I strove to model the kind of collaborative, servant leadership that I longed for and wanted to see, and to develop others and give them the opportunity to step into their own definitions of leadership.

Today, I continue to learn and grow as a leader every single day, knowing that this process will never end.

3. Negotiation Training

Are there things about your clinic, hospital, staff, home, community, or life in general that you wish were different? Do you feel you deserve more pay? Better benefits? More support? Less time on-call? More schedule flexibility? More help at home? If you are thinking "yes," then you will benefit from negotiation!

In the business world, there's a common saying: "You don't get what you deserve, you get what you negotiate." We found this to be true in medicine too. This was surprising, because we were incredibly accustomed to earning what we wanted by working extra hard. As it turns out, "going the extra mile" doesn't always get you what you need or want. Negotiation gives you a better chance.

Since you might not learn this incredibly valuable skill in medical school or residency, we recommend you learn negotiation as soon as possible thereafter. Remember: you are incredibly valuable as a woman physician; like a Tiffany diamond, you are rare, precious, and worth a lot! Learning your value and learning negotiation will help you understand your worth and how to get what you need and want, fast.

> **Evidence that negotiation is a valuable skill.** Studies show that a woman who does **not** negotiate her starting salary upon graduation will go without an average of $7,000 the first year and will lose between $650,000 and $1 million over the course of a 45-year career.[37] Assuming you retire at age 65, the average length of a physician's career is between 31 and 36 years.[38] Research indicates that 20% of women never negotiate at all, which means that women physicians are at risk of losing a substantial sum of money—money that could be used towards paying off

student debt and living a life of greater financial freedom. In addition to pay, things such as relocation expenses, vacation/PTO time, clinic/office resources, better or more support staff, work title, call schedules, continuing medical education (CME), maternity leave, remote work, telemedicine work, childcare, full-time equivalent (FTE) status, and help from others at home can be negotiated to make our lives better.

Why are women not negotiating? Research informs us that we are afraid of backlash and of not being liked.[39] So how can we overcome these fears and barriers to negotiation? Luckily, negotiation is a skill that anyone can learn and master with the right training and practice. We recommend taking a negotiation course or workshop to learn this skill. As we see it, if you can learn how to insert a central line into an ICU patient while being sleep deprived from overnight call, you can learn how to negotiate!

Notable benefits of negotiation training. The specific benefits of structured negotiation training include:

- Gaining the confidence to ask for what you want, need, and deserve
- Knowing your best alternatives to a negotiated agreement
- Cultivating positive emotions about negotiation
- Boosting your emotional intelligence
- Enhancing your financial wellness
- Improving the well-being of your family and community

HOW WE PERSONALLY BENEFITTED FROM NEGOTIATION TRAINING

Luisa's Story

I did not know anything about negotiation until I had to deal with a ridiculous problem. I was in my first job out of fellowship, a position that left me at my wits' end. I didn't need more money; I just needed to wash my hands and to have enough space to keep on schedule when seeing my daily load of patients. Was that too much to ask?

You see, as the new physician in my clinic, I was given only one exam room for my 20 patients per day, even when every other physician in my medical group had at least two. If this was not bad enough, my only exam room did not have a sink! At the start of my job, my initial thoughts were, "Okay, no biggie. I'll simply email my department head and request a transfer to a different clinic, one where I can have at least two fully equipped exam rooms like everyone else." Expecting to get a "Yes, right away," I sent the email immediately. To my dismay, the answer was "No." I was stunned!

My assumption that I could ask my employer for what I needed and easily get it was so wrong! At that moment, I felt defeated, irritated, and stuck. After tormenting myself for months with feelings of frustration, resentment, and anger every time I had to use the hand sanitizer (because I didn't have a freaking sink!), I finally learned about negotiation. I took a course, read a couple books, worked with an expert, and developed the skills necessary to increase my ability to creatively solve this problem for myself and everyone involved.

When I felt more prepared, I again approached my organization and presented a solution that was a win-win for myself, my clinic, and my employer. This time I got my "yes." To this day, I continue to work for the same employer and have all the resources I need to thrive as a physician.

Because I've had tremendous success since learning how to negotiate effectively and, more important, to not be scared about negotiating, I feel very strongly about helping all women physicians learn this important skill. I don't think the 45-minute PowerPoint presentation we're given at a national medical conference can cut it. Anyone serious about learning this skill needs to take a course and invest the time. You also need to practice.

My new mantra is,

"Everything is negotiable."

And knowing this has made my work life and home life easier. I promise you, if you can learn medicine, you can learn negotiation and be excellent at it!

4. Mindful Self-Compassion

Mindful self-compassion is a proven tool used to improve our emotional and physical well-being. As physicians, we strive to be wonderful healers, yet we are particularly vulnerable to anxiety, stress, overload, unhealthy self-criticism, self-judgments, and compassion fatigue because of our competitive training and our emotionally exhausting work environments. Having compassion for others starts with having compassion for ourselves. In Dr. Kristin Neff's research, self-compassion includes self-kindness, a sense of common humanity—that we are not alone in our imperfections—and mindfulness. Both mindfulness and self-compassion involve an attitude of curiosity and non-judgment towards our unique experiences.

> **Evidence that mindful self-compassion works.** Abundant evidence supports the power of mindful self-compassion! In this section we'll highlight a few key papers that support the use of self-compassion by physicians.
>
> In 2019, Medical Sciences published the results of a survey on the relationship between self-compassion and professional well-being (work engagement, exhaustion, and professional life satisfaction) among physicians in Canada. The study surveyed 57 practicing physicians: 65% were females, 47% were in the early career stage, 49% were family medicine physicians, and the rest were non-family medicine specialists. The results revealed that self-compassionate physicians experienced more positive work engagement, felt less emotionally, physically, and cognitively exhausted due to work demands, and were more satisfied with their professional life than physicians

who exhibited less compassion toward themselves in uncertain and challenging times.40

Similar benefits to physicians were reported by the *British Journal of General Practice*. In this study, 54 physicians completed eight weeks of mindfulness training. The researchers found that these doctors were more aware of their own feelings and thoughts, and were able to better accept situations, experience more peacefulness, and have more openness with themselves and others.[41]

Notable benefits of mindful self-compassion. Among the benefits of practicing mindful self-compassion, physicians report

- Increased emotional well-being
- Less judgement and criticism towards oneself and others
- Greater attitude of curiosity
- Lower levels of perceived stress, anxiety, and depression
- Increased levels of happiness, optimism, self-efficacy, and resilience
- Healthier lifestyles
- More rewarding relationships
- Stronger belief that we are human, we are not perfect, we fail, we make mistakes (and that it's okay!)

How we personally benefitted from mindful self-compassion. Prior to learning about mindful self-compassion we were both struggling with anxiety, compassion fatigue, overwhelm, and emotional exhaustion. It was difficult to quiet our minds. We often thought about our to-do lists, the clinic notes we needed to finish, the patients we worried about, the things our kids and pets needed, and the endless chores to be done at home. It was exceedingly difficult to stop thinking only of others!

Thankfully, our physician peer recommended that we check out a six-week course on mindful self-compassion. During that course, we learned how to quiet our minds by meditation, how to approach ourselves with kindness, and how to speak lovingly to ourselves—just the way our caring friends talk to us when we are feeling down or are being hard on ourselves. This approach brought tremendous peace and calm to our minds and bodies.

Learning to become more compassionate with ourselves required practice, like a muscle that needed to be strengthened. But we did it! We took the time to train ourselves to quiet our thoughts and focus inward on our current state of mind. We learned to ask "What do I need right now in this moment to feel safe, calm, or happy? To feel like I'm good enough?" With more practice, we experienced greater ease at slowing down our thoughts and feeling more centered.

We still have tough hospital days when we feel drained, but these are much less frequent because of our ongoing self-compassion practice.

5. Parenthood and Family Support

Medical training has conditioned us to perform at high standards, to strive for excellence, to be competent and independent, and to avoid delegating and asking others for help. When it comes to parenthood, though, these qualities will backfire, because it's simply unreasonable to hold ourselves to such high standards. We can't be perfect in all of our roles or be there for everyone and do it all, all the time! Unlike in medical school, kids need to see our imperfections and watch us fail. And our families need us to ask for help so we can feel relaxed and at our best. We understand this is easier said than done. Therefore, we recommend expert parenting support that helps make this part of our lives easier and more satisfying.

We want to acknowledge that these resources do not address the support needed at the institutional level, such as paid maternity and paternity leave, adequate breast pumping time without penalty, on-site childcare, and schedule flexibility. We agree that these resources would likely provide the greatest direct assistance to help physician families and working physician mothers thrive.

Outside of institutional support, though, we found tremendous value in working with an experienced parenting coach to help us with the challenges of being a first-time mom, managing work-family life, and parenting, all while practicing as physicians. Our family life was enriched by learning practical tools that helped us parent more peacefully and joyfully. This harmony at home made it easier to show up as our best selves at work.

Notable benefits of parenthood and family support.
After taking the time to access these resources, we each experienced:

- More peace and joy regarding parenthood
- More confidence being a mom
- Greater harmony at home

- Fewer power struggles with our kids
- Less stress when managing tantrums
- Greater ease in sharing the workload at home
- Stronger and more enjoyable family relationships

PERSONAL BENEFITS OF PARENTHOOD AND FAMILY SUPPORT

Luisa's Story

When my daughter was born, I was introduced to a new set of unanticipated challenges that would forever change my life as a practicing physician.

These challenges and complexities spanned from how to feed and sleep-train my child (Breastfeed? Bottle feed? Purees? Solids? Swaddles? Cry it out?), to coping with "Mommy guilt," to childcare dilemmas, to changes in relationship dynamics with my spouse, friends, and family members, to spending quality time with my child after exhausting clinic days, to time management and self-care, to altered workplace perceptions from patients, staff, and colleagues as the new "working mom," and the question, "How committed is she really?" The tricky thing about becoming a parent is that these challenges never really go away. As your child grows and your family expands, new challenges affect your life in a different way.

Unlike training to become a physician, there is no Parenting University or Parenting Residency or even a handy *Physician's Pocket Parenting* book that prepares one for this process! After "trying everything"—books, therapists, family therapists, parenting classes—I finally found a resource that worked: a wonderful parenting coach offered a course on "Parenting with Positive Discipline," teaching practical skills that I use daily with my children. Of the many helpful skills I learned, most transformational for me was shifting from an authoritarian parenting style to an authoritative parenting style.

Authoritative parents teach and guide their children, as opposed to authoritarian parents who control and emotionally coerce their children. I'm convinced that my "top-down" medical training influenced me toward becoming an authoritarian parent. Learning how to undo this training and become an authoritative parent allowed me to develop a more enjoyable, respectful, and collaborative relationship with my child.

Getting professional parenthood support helped me to gain new skills and confidence as a parent and to feel less stressed as a full-time physician and mom. I trust now in "progress over perfection." I strongly believe in the benefits of getting professional parenting support early on and invite you to check out the positive parenting resources we offer at Pink Coat MD.com!

1. Peer Support

We've found tremendous healing by having a safe, confidential, supportive network of other women physicians who understand our unique experiences. Did you know that learning from peers can be just as effective as mentorship or sponsorship? For example, as human beings, we are hard-wired for connection. Some of the toughest experiences we face as female physicians in medicine are feelings of isolation, stress, anxiety, and guilt. We feel as though we are the only ones going through this experience, and we feel alone. However, knowing through the power of community that this is a shared human experience is incredibly healing.

Evidence that peer support works. Studies have shown that peer learning can be an effective way to introduce new resources. Regularly scheduled, small groups reflecting on common themes have been shown to help us feel that we are not alone, and that we have shared experiences in our medical training and practice. Physicians who have participated in peer support programs appreciated the feeling of being heard in a nonjudgmental context. They also appreciate receiving practical and helpful information from their respected colleagues.[42,43,44]

Notable benefits of peer support. To summarize the findings on physician peer support, general benefits include:

- Less isolation and loneliness
- Shared humanity
- Connection
- Camaraderie
- New friendships

Next, Tammie shares her story of the positive effects of peer support.

THE PERSONAL BENEFITS OF PEER SUPPORT

Tammie's Story

Our idea for Pink Coat, MD came out of my experience in a children's hospital, where I had created a community peer group called "Cool Chicks in Medicine." The group started with two female colleagues meeting for dinner once a month and soon grew to a community of almost 250 women across our healthcare system. The otter became our mascot, and "We Support Each Otter" became our mantra. Before we knew it, we found that we had become each other's raft of otters, supporting each other in stormy seas.

In this group, I witnessed the tremendous power of camaraderie, community, and peer support, and I knew that this was the kind of experience I wanted to create for every single woman physician. At Pink Coat, MD we want each woman to feel like she has her own raft of otters, her own wolfpack to lift her up and to support her in tough times.

USEFUL LIFE STRATEGIES

We learned about these life strategies after benefitting from many of the professional resources we described above. Unfortunately, some valuable resources (such as professional coaching) can be expensive, and most healthcare organizations do not provide this service as a covered benefit or a service that one can purchase using their continuing medical education (CME) or business expense funds. That's why we will share with you some of the most valuable lessons we've learned from our experience having access to these important resources.

The practical—and free—life strategies that made the most meaningful difference and provided the greatest benefits to our lives as physicians include:

- Prioritizing self-care
- Letting go of guilt
- Reframing "work-life balance" as "work-life integration and harmony"
- Embracing personal boundaries
- Practicing self-compassion
- Knowing our values
- Connecting with our tribe

How do these strategies sound to you? If they sound quite foreign, that's okay! No one in our medical bubble had ever discussed these concepts, so we were unfamiliar with them, too, until we searched for solutions to our personal burnout back in 2015. Now that we have years of experience using these strategies, we can tell you confidently that you will experience some relief and improvement by knowing about these strategies and (hopefully) by incorporating them into your life.

WHAT'S NEXT?

Now that you know more about these resources, you may be wondering, "How do I find a professional coach? Take a mindful self-compassion class? Find an experienced parenting coach? Join a peer support group?" We invite you to enjoy easier access to each of these professional resources at PinkCoatMD.com.

Please let us save you time and endless research! Read the following chapters to learn more about each one of these life-changing strategies.

KEY MESSAGES

Although major systemic factors negatively affect our experience as women physicians, in our own lifetimes, we have learned to neutralize these harms by focusing on factors we can each control.

We encourage you to try the professional resources that helped us personally: professional coaching, leadership development, negotiation training, mindful self-compassion, parenthood and family support, and peer support.

We also recommend these practical life strategies that helped us cope with our imperfect experiences: prioritizing self-care, letting go of guilt, reframing "work-life balance" as "work-life integration and harmony," embracing personal boundaries, practicing self-compassion, knowing our values, and connecting with our tribe.

CHAPTER 04

CARE FOR YOURSELF FIRST AND IMPROVE YOUR ENERGY

BY LUISA DURAN, MD

TAKE CARE OF YOURSELF FIRST; YOU CAN'T POUR FROM AN EMPTY CUP.

Unknown

I learned the hard way how to put myself first. For years I had thought of others before myself—my patients, my colleagues, my family, my friends, my community—everyone first and myself always last. I remember coming home after a long day at the clinic, opening the door to see my three little kids jumping for joy, excited to see me, and my five-year-old saying, "Mommy, let's play!" At that moment, all I wanted to do was to head straight to the couch, curl up in a ball, and pass out like a vegetable. After seeing patients back-to-back every 20 minutes since 8 a.m., I was drained.

This went on for months, to a point where I worried there was something physically wrong with me. Despite plenty of sleep, healthy eating, and regular exercise, I would wake up the next morning exhausted. Have I developed hypothyroidism? Anemia? Diabetes? I decided to get checked out by my PCP. She ran a bunch of tests, then said, "Luisa, you're fine." I couldn't believe it. I double-checked the labs myself, and, sure enough, all the results were normal. I was confused and perplexed because I knew there was *something* wrong. So, I did what I sometimes tell my patients not to do: I did an internet search, listing my symptoms, and sure enough learned that I was experiencing emotional exhaustion, a typical symptom of physician burnout.

According to the Mayo Clinic, emotional exhaustion occurs when stress begins to accumulate from negative or challenging events that just keep coming. This repeated stress leaves us feeling emotionally worn out and drained. For most of us, emotional exhaustion slowly builds over time. We gradually experience symptoms like anxiety, nervousness, irritability, apathy, depression, feeling hopeless, powerless, trapped, and unmotivated. Sound familiar? We can develop physical symptoms like fatigue, headaches, lack of appetite, and sore or tense muscles. Inevitably, these symptoms affect our health, our relationships, our performance at work, and our home life.[45] And as it turns out, emotional exhaustion is the most common symptom of burnout experienced by women physicians.

For me, emotional exhaustion manifested as feeling more irritable, anxious, hopeless, and physically tired. I was often cranky, and my irritability would show up when dealing with difficult patients or at home when my kids tested my patience. I was easily triggered by the smallest slights. Soon I was snapping at my husband and yelling at my kids over silly, childish squabbles. I was not the person I wanted to be for myself or my family and was certainly not modeling the woman I wanted my daughter to become. I was losing the best of myself, and I also stopped bringing out the best in those most near and dear to me. What was I to do?

I must admit, I felt a little embarrassed and ashamed about searching and asking for help. I wasn't comfortable with being vulnerable, and I didn't want people to think I was weak or that there was something wrong with me. I didn't want others to worry about me, especially my parents and husband who were already stressed, or my young children who look up to me for ... well ... everything. I was also worried that this would somehow be discovered by my employer and damage my career or the professional reputation that I had worked so hard to build and perfect. And I was humiliated at the thought that my patients might learn about my struggles and no longer feel comfortable with me as their physician. In short, I was scared to lose my intrinsic value and the respect of others.

What motivated me to finally act and get the help I needed? I think I just got tired of being a chronically exhausted, overweight, irritable, grumpy, and anxious person. I got tired of looking at myself in the mirror and seeing a woman I no longer recognized. I wasn't my joyful, energetic, smiling self. I forgot how to play and have fun. I was secretly jealous of all my patients who were happy, thriving, and enjoying life, and I felt sad that I couldn't have the same experience. Most motivating, though, was that I didn't want to keep modeling this tired, grumpy, and serious person (the person I'm convinced I morphed into during my medical training and immersion within the healthcare culture) to my children, especially my daughter.

So how did I get help? By good fortune, I found a wonderful, loving, and supportive coach who understood my experience. She helped me start a new path of taking care of me first. I learned many useful strategies that changed the trajectory of my professional life and helped me reclaim my energy. These were small actions that I could easily implement in my busy life and that gave me benefits beyond just better sleep, healthy eating, and more exercise. Because they are incredibly simple yet life-changing, I want to share the three most effective small actions, those that I believe you can easily implement and benefit from starting today.

KNOW WHAT YOU NEED

Know what you need to be at your best. And yes, it took time and working with a professional for me to finally ask myself every day, "What do I need to be at my best? Today? This week? This month? This year? What do I need?" I discovered the answer to this question for me could be big or small and different each day. Some big things could be the need to feel respected, valued, and heard in my workplace and my home. It could also be simple things, like taking care of my body and resting my mind. For example, after a long day of seeing a ton of patients back-to-back, what I sometimes need to feel my best is a thirty-minute foot massage to soothe and relax my body. Or when I have a full day of clinic, I need to *physically* leave for my lunch break, so that I can breathe fresh air, feel the sunshine on my skin, walk, and re-energize myself for my afternoon patients.

I want to ask you the same question: "What do you need to be at your best?" I invite you to take a moment now to think about this. What's something that excites you, an action that brings personal joy? What's something you can do this week to feel your best?

These are simple questions, but if you're like me and are wired to care about others, it can be hard to come up with answers beyond the obvious (exercise, eating healthily and getting plenty of sleep, et cetera). So, I love this list of thought-starters as shared by our fabulous women's empowerment coach Betsy Flanagan, MBA. It helps jog our minds with ideas about simple ways to cultivate joy in our everyday lives.

THOUGHT STARTERS FOR JOY

- Take a bubble bath.
- Spend time in nature.
- Go away for the night or longer.
- Enjoy a "Me Day" or a day at the spa.

- Write down what you're grateful for.
- Enjoy time with a group of friends, or one-on-one time, or alone, quiet time.
- Feel the sunshine on your skin.
- Focus on the present moment, not the past or future.
- Wear something that makes you feel good.
- Just be!
- Get a massage.
- Eat a meal you enjoy.
- Watch an entertaining, uplifting movie.
- Stay in your PJs—all day
- Hug your loved ones.
- Hire help.

MAKE A SCHEDULE THAT WORKS FOR YOU

My second small action is scheduling what you need in your calendar. Make your quiet time or bubble bath a priority. Write that down first, even before you schedule your next call, conference, virtual meeting, or family commitment. For the longest time my schedule was full of work- and family-related activities. Just looking at my monthly calendar gave me stress. Now, I enjoy glancing at my day, week, or month in advance, because there are treats just for me in there, too. As I'm writing this, I see that tonight at 7 p.m. I will be joining my other women physician friends for a yoga and meditation class with our amazing, lovely instructor. Just knowing that it is scheduled in my calendar brings me joy and excitement to get through my next ten afternoon clinic patients.

RELEASE GUILT

My third small action is to let go of guilt. Are you feeling guilty that you're going to read a fun novel, practice painting, meet with a friend, or get a full-body massage on a Thursday afternoon, instead of finishing your chart notes, taking on one extra medical case, picking up your kid from school, or cooking dinner for your family? It's okay if you have these feelings! I struggled with this guilt for years, especially after having children. Self-care guilt is a common experience and shows up in various ways, such as apologizing for yourself, feeling like you're being selfish or indulgent, or pushing self-care activities off because you have "more important things to do." You might even have a voice in your head telling you that you are selfish for doing something for yourself.

How can we redefine self-care so that we don't feel guilty about it? One approach is to view self-care as a necessary medicine for your physical, mental, emotional, and spiritual well-being. It is not about being selfish, indulgent, or escaping your life. It's about becoming your best self and living your best life. It's about valuing yourself enough to do what it takes to be full of energy and in good health, so that you can continue as your high-performing self. As I tell my patients, your health and wellness are loving gifts to your family!

Another approach is to remember all of the positive benefits of taking good care of yourself. Self-care gives you energy to meet the demands of your work and your busy life, helps you to stay calm under pressure, increases your ability to focus and be more productive, and helps you to manage your emotions so that you more quickly recover from emotional triggers. By investing in yourself with small everyday self-care actions, you become equipped for success at work and at home. Proper self-care enables you to be of greater service to your family, your children, your friends, your elderly parents, your patients, and your community.

As women physicians who work full-time and have full lives outside of our clinical work, it is imperative that we take care of ourselves first, even before our patients, our families, and our communities, ***so that*** we will have the health, energy, stamina, physical, mental, emotional, and social well-being to best care for and heal others.

KEY MESSAGES

Identify what you need to feel your best each day/week/month/year and make that activity a priority by scheduling it first in your calendar, ahead of all other commitments.

Do not feel guilty or indulgent about prioritizing your needs before those of your patients, your family, or anyone else in your life. Self-care is vital to your well-being and allows you to be your best self in the world.

We've learned that one can spiral quickly into a miserable person when not prioritizing self-care. This happened because our medical training programmed us to care for others before ourselves. We urge you to take care of yourself first, so you do not fall into this trap!

CHAPTER 05

GOODBYE WORK-LIFE BALANCE, HELLO WORK-LIFE INTEGRATION

BY LUISA DURAN, MD

IF I'M PURSUING MY GOALS, MY KIDS ARE SEEING ME AT MY BEST... I ALWAYS REMEMBER THAT A HAPPY WORKING WOMAN IS A HAPPY MOTHER.

Shonda Rhimes

As a full-time practicing physician with three young kids at home, I'm often asked, "How do you balance your work and life?" Or "How are you doing it all?" As it turns out, work life-balance is a top concern among female physicians under the age of 45, even more so than pay. In a recent Medscape survey of more than 3,000 women physicians, 63% responded that work-life balance was their top struggle.[46]

As a female physician who has worked non-stop since getting my medical degree at age 27, I feel this concern too. When I finally had a life outside of medicine, I was more affected by this because of feelings of guilt. The more hours I spent working, the more I would feel guilty about not being with my family. This was exacerbated when I became a mother and felt even more pressure to be at home with my babies and more guilt when I was working. I even had patients, colleagues, and my own parents question my choice to work full-time after becoming a mother. "Are you sure you want to work full-time?" "Who will take care of your kids?" "The early years of your kids' lives are precious; you don't want to miss out. They grow up so fast!" I've asked my husband if he's ever heard such comments, and his answer is a flat "no."

I didn't know at the time, but I now understand these comments are rooted in what's known as **maternal wall bias**. Research by law professor Joan C. Williams has brought to light the stereotyping of mothers in the workplace. (I invite you to learn in more depth about the phenomenon of maternal wall bias by reading the work of Professor Joan C. Williams, which is widely reported on various internet sites.) Successful working women may suddenly find their proficiency questioned after they become mothers. And if these working mothers remain committed to their jobs, others may accuse them of being insufficiently maternal. It's another subtle barrier that no one really talks about.

How do I overcome this "guilt" and these subtle barriers

associated with being a full-time working physician mother? How do I find "balance"? First, I stopped using the word "balance" or even thinking about "work-life balance," because, to me, balance implies competition and cost. If I am working, then I am missing out on my home life. If I am home, then I am not giving my all to my work; in other words, I'm slacking. Either way, I am missing out. I can't win. And with this mindset, there's fear, guilt and maybe some shame.

Knowing the facts about working parents has also helped with this healthier mindset. Did you know that years of research dating back to the 1990's on children's development affirm that working is *okay* for children? Daily absences of employed mothers do *not* harm the attachment between the mother and her child. In not a single analysis is the mother's employment status related to the way a child sees his or her mother or father. Neither is her working part-time or full-time. It is who the mother is as a *person* and the *relationship* she establishes with her child that are the important factors. Studies have found again and again that when mothers are doing what they think is right for themselves and their families, their children are more likely to prosper. In other words, your attitude about working—whether you believe you are doing the right thing either by working or by being at home—is what's most important to your child.[47] Furthermore, children learn more about the world of work from their mothers than they do from their fathers. And in a new study of 50,000 adults in 25 countries, daughters of working mothers completed more years of education, were more likely to be employed and in supervisory roles, and earned higher incomes.[48]

So, what if we eliminated the word "balance?" And in place of balance, we used the word "integration?" Or "harmony?" Or "synergy?"

Any of these alternatives imply we can spend time at work, invest time in our health and well-being, and spend time at home to be our best selves. Words are powerful, and these eliminate the false choice presented to women to be either parents or breadwinners (quite ridiculous, considering they are winning the bread to feed their families!) and allow the same room to breathe that has *always* been available to fathers. They also eliminate the subtle suggestion that there should be two separate calendars, two caches of time available to one human being: one for work and the other for parenting. Instead, mothers can sanely acknowledge that they each have only 24 hours each day—and that is enough.

When I started to think about myself as a person who integrates her role as a full-time physician into her life as full-time mother, wife, daughter, friend, and community leader, I was transformed for the better. I was no longer weighed down by the guilt I once felt for working in my full-time clinic, which sometimes kept me at work well past dinnertime. Or needing to work four or five days a week and not being "that mom" who dropped off my son at his preschool, picked up my daughter from kindergarten, and played with my kids every day at the playground. Or the "perfect" wife, daughter, and friend, one who is "always there" for everything and everyone.

Instead, I was liberated from what was draining my energy and limiting my potential. I was free to gain richness and strength from performing at my highest level, using my unique, hard-earned skills to diagnose life-threatening diseases, prescribe life-saving therapies, and change people's lives for the better. Our amazing work as physicians now fuels me to be a better mom at home! I don't sweat the small stuff, like when my kids spill milk on the floor for the hundredth time, wear their clothes backwards to school, or smear poop on the walls (true story). I also embrace the value of modeling for my daughter a woman who loves her work and is not beating herself up or feeling guilty or resentful about not being the "perfect Mom."

I am not alone in this desire to change how we model success to our daughters. Take in for a moment the powerful words of Shonda Rhimes, creator of the iconic *Grey's Anatomy*, the most popular physician TV show of all time:

"All the greeting cards are about sacrifice. 'Mother, you gave up so much for me. You worked so hard for me. You sacrificed so much. You were so wonderful and giving and selfless.' Where is the greeting card that says, 'Mother, you taught me how to be a powerful woman,' 'Mother, you taught me how to earn a living,' 'Mother, you taught me how to speak up for myself and not back down?' Those are the greeting cards that should be out there. Those are the qualities that we would want for our daughters to have. I don't want my daughters to grow up and think, 'I should shrink and be in the background. I should be selfless. I should be sacrificing. I should be silent.' That's not what I think a mother is."[49]

I love this quote, because as women physicians we are that message! We are teaching our daughters how to be powerful, how to earn a living, how to use their voices, and so much more! Don't you agree? I can't imagine a more credible source for this kind of wisdom than a Hollywood titan, one who understands life as a working professional woman and a totally devoted single mother raising three daughters!

Finally, I'd like to highlight the words from my respected and beloved meds/peds colleague who, like Shonda Rhimes, is devoted to her three young children:

"We need to learn to show ourselves that same compassion we would show others, and stop with the mom guilt, because we are all awesome moms. Our kids are going to be just fine."

Now that you've had some time to think about an alternative to "work-life balance," how does the idea of integration feel to you? Easier, perhaps? How can you become your best self at work? At home? In all aspects of your life?

I hope you feel relief in understanding that you can be the same person at work and at home, and that it is not about balancing. Rather, it's about integrating yourself in everything that you do! This harmonizing of identities truly helped me embrace becoming that amazing, professional woman "who does it all." Maybe it will for you too. When the guilt starts creeping in (and it probably will, because you're only human), try to remember that you are better at all your roles because of how you are nourishing yourself in and outside of work.

Finally, when my patient or anyone at work asks, "How are you working and raising three kids?" I simply answer, "Being a physician makes me a better, happier mom, and being a mom makes me a better, happier physician." Period.

KEY MESSAGES

Think about life and work as integration and harmony, and not as "work-life balance," (which promotes the feeling that life and work are in competition). There is no balancing act, only integration.

We can be the same people at home, at work, and everywhere in between.

Who are you when you are your best self?

What might need to change so that you can show up as your best self in all areas of your life?

CHAPTER 06

EMBRACING PERSONAL BOUNDARIES

BY TAMMIE CHANG, MD

MY DEEPEST WISH IS FOR YOU TO DISCOVER AND CREATE THIS SACRED SPACE <u>FOR YOU</u>. BOUNDARIES START WITH YOU, FROM WITHIN.

Tammie Chang, MD

I think I am so deeply passionate about boundaries because not having them was why I found myself in the darkest place of my life: severely burned out and suicidal only five years into my practice as a pediatric hematologist/oncologist. While I'd learned about boundaries earlier, I didn't really get what it meant. I hadn't internalized the concept.

After several months of collective personal tragedy and hardship in our community practice, we were short-staffed, with too few physicians and a record number of new cancer diagnoses, while covering a high-acuity, 24/7 pediatric hematology/oncology service. Our colleague and his family were also struggling with the most difficult experience of their lives: their daughter ultimately losing her battle with metastatic cancer. We were trying to support him while giving him space and grace, shouldering the load as we would for any close friend, family member, or colleague.

I felt tremendous responsibility and pressure to step up, to hold our group and our staff together, and to soldier on with no clear end to the overwhelming workload in sight. I worked every other week on service and also every other weekend, taking more overnight calls than I ever had as a resident or fellow. I hadn't slept in months, I had gained more than 20 pounds, and I was constantly anxious and worried about our staff, our clinic, and my colleagues. I spent hours working on weekends and until late into the night, reaching out to other professional groups and practices for help and back up, interviewing temporary staffing candidates, and caring for our bursting inpatient service.

During this time, I had no idea that I was heading into the dark miasma of what would turn out to be severe burnout, suicidal ideation, and breakdown. It was not until one weekend afternoon on call, after I had spent several hours sitting with a family—holding space for them as they bravely chose to withdraw life support from their son, who had cancer—that I knew I was done. And as I drove home from work that day, I found that all I could think about was driving my car off a cliff, so that I wouldn't have to return to work the next day.

Thankfully, I didn't. I chose instead to ask for help. And what has come out of that time in my life is a burning desire to support other physicians, especially women, not to reach the point where they so desperately need help. Looking back, I understand that my lack of internal personal boundaries was the reason that I reached such a dark place. I now think about gentle, healthy boundaries every single day, and this is one of the key reasons why today I am thriving.

WHAT ARE BOUNDARIES?

When I bring this concept up with colleagues and friends, clients and audience members, there is a shared outcry of resistance, followed immediately by guilt. When I ask women to share an image or metaphor of what boundaries mean to them, they present images of prisons with barbed wire fences, fortresses on islands surrounded by vast waters, or of a person drawing a dark, thick line in the sand, saying, "NO."

Why do we have such a visceral, gut response to this concept, especially as women and as physicians?

One reason might be the double whammy of societal pressure as women and as physicians. We are conditioned and socialized from a very early age to be a "good girl," which often means to please others and to be well-liked. This manifests as **human giver syndrome** in adulthood as mothers, wives, co-workers, caretakers, friends, and physicians.[50]

Another reason: two decades of conditioning and the

indoctrination into the culture of medicine. As physicians we are trained from the very beginning of medical school to put the patient, everyone, and everything first, before our own needs. We are taught that to be a good physician means doing everything we can for our patient. To go "above and beyond" at all times.

There is absolutely virtue in this. As individuals, we entered the field of medicine because we felt deeply called to become physicians, to serve others, and to heal the sick and the dying. For many of us, becoming physicians began with a deep desire to give and to serve, beginning at a young age.

What is missing from our centuries-old culture of medicine, however, is the recognition (and training) that to best care for patients and others, we must care for ourselves *first*. We must come to work ready to work, refreshed, and rested, having attended to our own needs. When we are burned out, emotionally and physically exhausted, and overwhelmed with compassion fatigue and cynicism, we are not the physicians we are capable of being. Each of us is not the woman, mother, wife, friend, sister, daughter, or human being she is capable of being.

What I want to offer readers is a kinder, gentler, and healthier way of thinking about boundaries and about what it means to care for ourselves first. When I work with other women physicians, together we visualize a beautiful home, surrounded by a flourishing garden, trees, and a well-cared for picket fence. The fence is not immense or impressive in any way, just there, freshly painted, with doors and latches. There might be a rocking chair, on the porch or in the shade, with a warm cup of tea on top of a coffee table. Maybe even a purring cat curled up on the step!

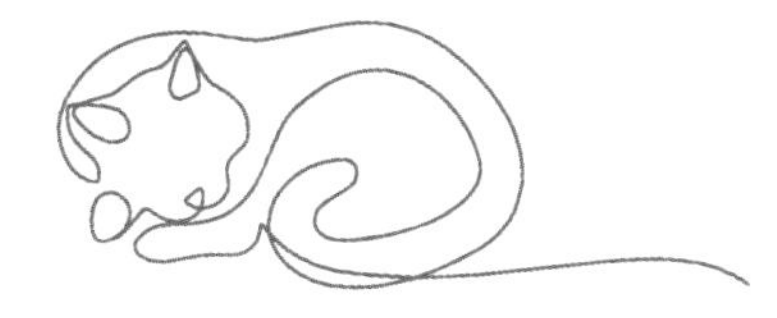

THOUGHT-STARTERS TO CREATE BOUNDARIES

Boundaries Start with You

- Notice when you have critical or judgmental thoughts. Create a boundary from these negative thoughts.
- When do you find yourself feeling guilty? When do you notice yourself saying "I should...?" This may be a clue that you are saying "yes" when you actually want to be saying "no."
- When do you notice yourself feeling nervous and scared, but also excited? This may be a clue that you are saying "no" when you actually want to be saying "yes."

Boundaries at Work

- Allow yourself to completely disconnect when you are not at work.
- Turn your pager off when you are not at work or on call.
- Take work email off your phone and don't check work email when you are off hours.
- Don't open your electronic medical record from home, EVER.

- Don't respond to text messages or phone calls from work unless you are on call. Don't respond to staff or work colleagues when you are on vacation.

- If you chart in an office, close the door. If you chart in an open area, put on headphones to signal to others that you are unavailable.

- Patient notes do not have to be works of art. Keep it short and to the point. B- or even C+ work is good enough! Put a boundary around perfectionism.

Boundaries at Home

- Turn off all phone notifications before you get home.

- Share the load. Ask for help from your partner, grandparents, extended family, and neighbors.

- Outsource or hire help when you can for cleaning, yard work, or other tasks that drain your energy.

- Designate your own special space and time at home when no one can bother you (unless it's a real emergency). This could be quiet time, reading, taking a bath, listening to music, enjoying yoga, or playing an instrument. Whatever brings you joy.

- Set clear boundaries around interactions with family, friends, and neighbors who may drain your energy.

- Put your phone away when you are spending time with loved ones.

Ask yourself:

- What do you want your home to look and feel like? Your inner sanctuary? What do you want to have in your garden?
- What do you want to have inside your fence? What needs to remain outside of your fence?
- What do you need to say "no" to?
- What belongs outside of your home and doesn't need to trigger or impact you negatively?
- And even more importantly, from another angle, what do you need to say "yes" to?
- What belongs inside of your fence, that perhaps you are scared, but a little excited, to let in?
- Where can you play bigger within your walls, in a way that most honors your most authentic, real, and honest you?

KEY MESSAGES

We have been conditioned as women and physicians from an early age to give, give, give. We have rarely seen healthy boundaries modeled for us during the decades it took us to become physicians.

Boundaries are your home, your garden, and everything within the walls of your picket fence. Boundaries do not have to be a castle surrounded by a moat filled with alligators, a prison with an electric barbed-wire fence, or a thick line in the sand drawn with a big fat "NO."

We can have a gentler, kinder, and healthier way of thinking about boundaries. Not only do we need to think about what belongs in our space, in our home and our yard, but also what belongs outside.

CHAPTER 07

THE POWER OF SELF-COMPASSION

BY TAMMIE CHANG, MD

TALK TO YOURSELF LIKE YOU WOULD TO SOMEONE YOU LOVE.

Brené Brown, PhD, LMSW

It wasn't until I hit rock bottom (as I shared in the previous chapter) that I truly began to understand what having self-compassion meant. I'd had an intermittent loving-kindness meditation and a hot yoga practice over the years, but "May I love and be kind to myself and others" would quickly revert to the overwhelming feelings of exhaustion, overwork, pleasing others, and self-criticism that had long been my default mode.

My hyper-achieving, perfectionist, eager-to-please, and hypercritical self emerged at an early age. The daughter of hard-working, Taiwanese immigrant parents, discipline and a strong work ethic were both drilled into me by the time I started pre-school. I began playing the cello at age four, and then added the piano at age six. Long daily hours of practice started young. Despite attending a special, accepting, and loving private school and being raised by deeply loving but strict parents, by the time I was five I had still internalized the critical, survival-oriented need to excel at everything.

And I did. By the time I was in high school, I was waking up by four a.m. to study and practice the piano before school; and I would study and practice the piano late into the night, usually until midnight or one a.m. And it was never good enough for me. Ask any athlete, musician, or dancer, and you will get a glimpse into the similar internal thoughts of high achievers in high-performance fields. I would spend hours practicing one phrase or even one measure, perfecting and perfecting the tone and execution of each note. And even then, it was never good enough—it could always be better.

My hyper-critical, hyper-achieving, needing-to-please internal monologue was only further developed in college and medical school, where we learned early on what it takes to survive: to put your own needs on the backburner and study, study, study. I was surrounded by other perfectionistic hyper-achievers, just like me.

And to survive, we had to please others—especially as medical students on the wards, then later as interns, residents, and fellows.

Yet when I had to stop and fully re-assess my life in its entirety, I began to read and immerse myself in resources that could help me *feel* better. This was when I discovered the work of Kristin Neff, PhD on self-compassion and the work of Brené Brown, PhD, LMSW (for the second time!). Somehow their words did not fully resonate until I hit my lowest point. That was when I began to learn and understand that our experiences of life are completely made up of the thousands of thoughts that run through our minds each day. What we say and think to ourselves, moment-to-moment, drives our emotions and ultimately our behavior and experience of our world. Have you noticed that our lives are a continuous internal monologue? Consider:

- What are you saying to yourself right now?
- What do you find yourself saying to yourself often?
- What is the quality of your thoughts? Are they kind? Loving? Compassionate?
- What would you say to a good friend or someone you love?

Through the work of Dr. Neff, we know that having a strong practice of self-compassion is highly correlated with decreases in anxiety, burnout, and depression, as well as improved relationships and connections and an overall improved well-being and quality of life.[51]

My co-author Luisa and I have learned this the hard way, having toiled and sacrificed our own needs and self-worth for so long. We were both always thinking, "This isn't good enough," or "I could do better," or "I'm not ready yet," or, "Gosh, who do I think I am?" Instead, we now love and say these phrases to ourselves constantly, every single day:

"You're doing great, sweetheart. You're doing the best you can."

"Oh, well."

"What do I need to be kind to myself right now?"

Try it. During the day, stop to write down the phrases that you say to yourself. Look at them. What do they sound like? Are they words of a good friend speaking to someone they love? When we have the courage to give ourselves the same self-compassion that we strive to give others, our world expands exponentially. And what a wonderful world that could be!

KEY MESSAGES

Through the work of Dr. Kristin Neff, we know that having a strong practice of self-compassion is highly correlated with decreased anxiety, burnout, and depression, with improved relationships and connection, and with overall improved well-being and quality of life.[52]

What is the quality of your thoughts? Are they the words of a good friend to someone they love?

What will be your go-to phrases to be kind to yourself? We shared a few in this short chapter. Use ours or create your own.

Go forth and give yourself the love you deserve.

CHAPTER 08

TO LIVE WITH GREATER EASE, KNOW YOUR VALUES

BY LUISA DURAN, MD

IT'S NOT HARD TO MAKE DECISIONS WHEN YOU KNOW WHAT YOUR VALUES ARE.

Roy Disney

What are values, and why is knowing our top values so important to helping us thrive? Values reflect what is most important to us; they form the core of our being. Our values influence how we think, feel, act, and shape the results we obtain in life.

One way to imagine our core values is to imagine them as our personal GPS systems. You wouldn't leave on a road trip without having a map or a guide, right? It's the same idea for how we live our lives! You need your values to point you in the direction of a meaningful and fulfilling life, full of passion and purpose, one that is true to who you are.

Many values can be your personal core values. If you search the web for "core values," you'll find lists with more than 200 to choose from. Achievement? Beauty? Bravery? Compassion? Discipline? Efficiency? Growth? Honesty? Independence? Knowledge? Justice? Power? Respect? Service? Status? Trust? The list goes on. Everyone can have their unique list of core values, and there can be many values on this list.

However, it's important to know your essential values as well. We recommend identifying your top five values, because by knowing these, you are more likely to think, feel, and behave in a way that's most aligned with your core being and to see results that are most meaningful to you. This alignment is incredibly important, because when your actions are not aligned you can feel miserable, defeated, and sad. You don't see the results you desire. This can be a form of suffering.

I personally experienced the agony that comes with not being aligned with my core values. Even after fellowship, I had never really considered them. Then I naively took a job at a clinic, one that, in retrospect, espoused different values than mine. The clinic had a strong culture of welcoming drug reps who practically lived at our office. Yet I had no clue about this when I signed my contract! While there was no overt coercion or pressure, my colleagues and all our office staff simply "loved" the drug reps and encouraged them to bring our Starbucks coffee in the morning, food from Nordstrom Café for lunch, and our favorite Jamba Juice as an afternoon snack.

While everyone else enjoyed these visits, I struggled. I felt uncomfortable seeing drug reps roaming our office. When I sat down to eat *their* lunch—because everyone else in my office was eating their lunch too—I felt at odds with myself. Over time, I felt unhappy and disgusted at my behavior. I realize now that I was experiencing the feeling of guilt and shame resulting from ignoring my core values.

The only way for me to escape this agony was to act to protect these ideals. I worked with a professional coach who helped me get crystal clear on my top values, then to devise a strategy to align my values with my workplace. I discovered that my feelings of shame arose because I felt that my integrity was compromised by my interaction with drug reps. Once I understood this, I developed the confidence to have a serious talk with my office partner and to negotiate a clinic policy where drug reps could no longer contact or meet with me. Everyone in my clinic understood that I did not accept lunches or samples and respected this firm decision. As a result, I felt greater satisfaction and enjoyment at my workplace and more at peace in my core being.

Getting clear on top values can also help with making decisions quickly. Have you ever struggled with making some kind of decision? We all have, right?! Life is full of these moments when we struggle to make quick decisions and to find direction in our daily life. These dilemmas are much easier, however, when we are crystal clear about our values.

For example, I recently struggled with a decision that could otherwise have broken my heart. It was a typical cold Thursday morning. I overslept, rushing around my house, trying to get myself and my little kids out the door so I could be on time for my eight-a.m. patient. Suddenly, I heard the cries and screams of my two-year-old son Peter, "Mommy, I can't open my eyes!" I turned to look at him in his bed, in his Spiderman pajamas, and saw both eyes sealed shut by gooey discharge. He had contracted a bad case of conjunctivitis at daycare.

At that moment I panicked, thinking, "Oh my goodness! What should I do?" Despite the love for my child, I found myself in a dilemma, struggling to quickly decide between two choices: should I call back-up care for my son so that I could get to work on time, or use my personal time so that I could care for my child? Then I remembered my patients. I had a clinic packed with twenty people who'd waited months to see me! If I canceled, those patients would be angry and perhaps not be able to see me for months. How could I disappoint them? What would my staff say? My colleagues might be very annoyed. What would my director think? Needless to say, I was really struggling, and I needed to act fast.

At that moment, I had to rely on my core values. Since "family" is one of my top values, I decided to call my office and let them know that I was staying home and taking PTO (personal time off). Done. And since I felt aligned to my core being, I felt a tremendous relief—like a big, belly breath exhalation that I had made the right decision for me. No guilt. No apologies. And guess what? When I returned to work, I was my best self and not weighed down by feelings of resentment.

I like to share this example, because to people outside of medicine, it may seem like a slam-dunk, easy dilemma to resolve. One might say, "Oh, well, of course you're going to stay home and take care of your sick kid. You're his mom, for goodness' sake!" In my life, I've noticed the assumption that because I am a mother,

I *must* stay home to care for my kids. However, as a physician who's taken the Hippocratic Oath, I must also consider my patients, and so these decisions are not easy.

I bet any working mother can relate to this struggle, to the dilemmas we experience when we need to decide between our families or our children and our work. It's not always a simple "of course I'm choosing my kids," or, "of course I'm choosing my elderly parents," or, "of course I'm choosing my family," answer. And physicians also feel the weight, the responsibility, and the added guilt that comes with being a very human physician.

I have found tremendous peace by doing the inner work of clarifying my values and knowing deep down that my family is my priority. I can more easily make decisions without the heaviness or the guilt that I experienced when I was not crystal clear on my values. Despite the oath that I took as a single, childless, relatively carefree 27-year-old, I now confidently know, as a 40-year-old responsible physician and parent of three young children, that my family comes first, *even before my patients*. Guess what I've learned from my patients? They admire this!

I hope these examples demonstrate the importance of knowing your top values. I invite you to consider:

- What's most important to me? Is it success? Achievement? Wealth? Family? Education? Health? Beauty? Service? Love? Loyalty?
- What are my top five values?
- How do you envision yourself when you are crystal clear and aligned with your core values?

I encourage you to write down what comes to mind. Don't worry if you're still processing. This is deep, reflective stuff. It took months for me to finally identify my values and years to make them crystal clear, and I still work at this every day. One benefit of becoming clearer about your values is that you can live your life with greater ease and harmony. Knowing my values has helped me live in flow. I now imagine myself as a powerful river, coursing effortlessly through an unknown forest in the direction of my dreams.

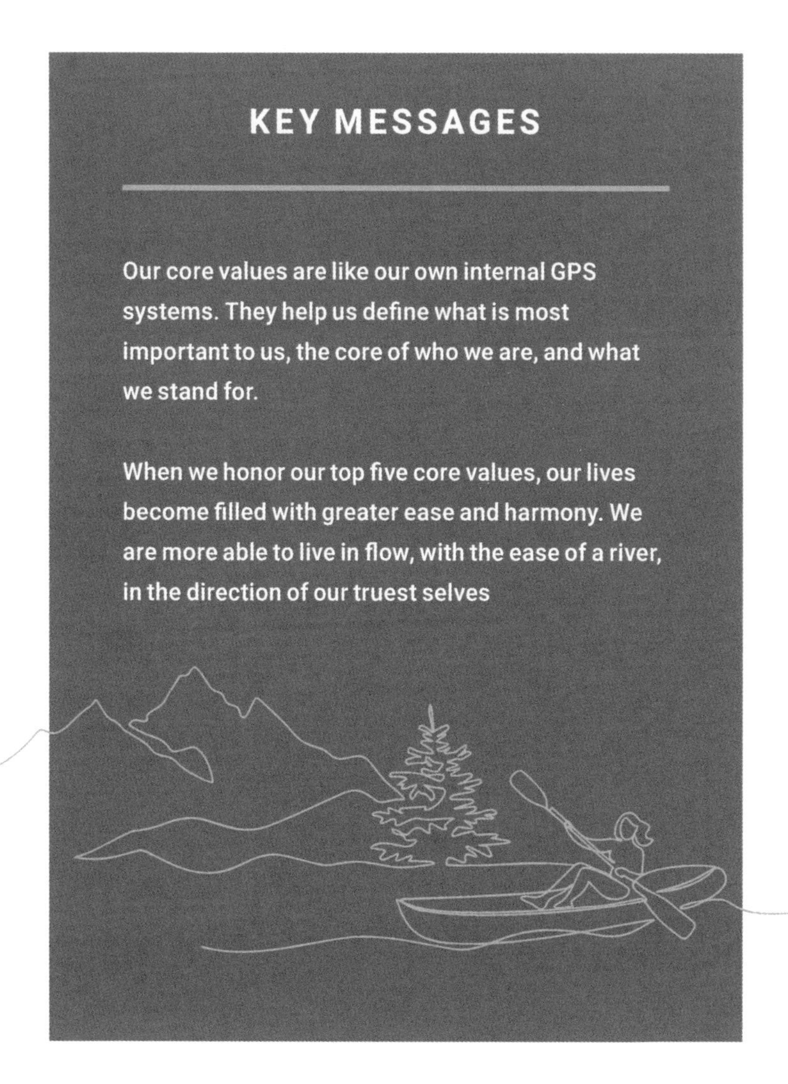

KEY MESSAGES

Our core values are like our own internal GPS systems. They help us define what is most important to us, the core of who we are, and what we stand for.

When we honor our top five core values, our lives become filled with greater ease and harmony. We are more able to live in flow, with the ease of a river, in the direction of our truest selves

CHAPTER 09

HEALING WITH CONNECTION AND CREATING OUR PACK

BY TAMMIE CHANG, MD

LIFE IS NOT MEANT TO BE LIVED AS A LONE WOLF. WE ALL NEED A PACK. HER VICTORY IS YOUR VICTORY. CELEBRATE WITH HER. YOUR VICTORY IS HER VICTORY. POINT TO HER.

Abby Wambach

At our core, we believe deeply in the power of connection to heal us as women, physicians, and human beings. We know and deeply believe that when we come together, we are exponentially greater than the sum of the individual parts. As human beings, we are wired for connection, belonging, and to love and be loved. And when we find our tribe, our wolf pack or the raft of otters who have our back, there is no stopping us.

As mentioned earlier in this book, female otters are known to band together in stormy seas to create a "raft" for protection and survival. Luisa and I and our Pink Coat, MD community have become just that, for each other. And we want you to find your own raft of otters, your own wolf pack, your people. We want you to feel like you belong and that you have friends and sisters who support you.

As women, many of us (sadly) have lived in a culture of "woman against woman," of the oppressed against the oppressed. How many of you have experienced this, either along gender or other lines? Of women being even harder on other women than they are with others? We certainly have. This comes as no surprise given the history of how women have struggled for equality in the workplace, in leadership, in opportunities, and in the home. And we still have so far to go. Before, there were few spots at the top for any woman, which sometimes caused women to try to bring down the women who had risen.

I deeply believe that there is room for all of us, for every person who wants to be at the table, and especially for every single young girl who aspires to one day have a voice at the table. I believe in having an infinite mindset, where there is no limit to what we can create, the size of our table, or how many chairs we can offer to others. I deeply believe that our world is a better world when all of us have a place at the table.

Allow me to challenge you:

- How will you create your raft of otters or your wolf pack AND invite others to join you?
- How will you commit to building a bigger table with enough seats for everyone?
- When we come together, we are exponentially greater than the sum of our individual parts.

KEY MESSAGES

As human beings, we are wired for connection, belonging, and to love and be loved. So, when we find our tribe, our wolfpack or the raft of otters who have our back, there is no stopping us.

Throughout history and even today, we have often experienced a culture of "woman against woman," of women trying to pull others down. Yet we have the capacity to rise above this.

How will you commit to create your raft of otters or your wolf pack AND invite others to join you? How will you commit to building a larger table with seats for all?

CHAPTER 10

BECOMING THE HOPE

BE THE CHANGE YOU WANT TO SEE IN THE WORLD.

Mahatma Gandhi

When Luisa's daughter was four years old, she caught her mother as she was leaving for clinic and said, "Mommy, I want to become a physician too." At that moment, Luisa's heart was filled with mixed feelings. On the one hand, she felt absolutely thrilled that her daughter wanted to follow in her footsteps. On the other hand, the parent in her felt terrified, because she didn't want her daughter to suffer in this harsh medical culture the way that she and many colleagues had suffered.

How can we make things better for our daughters and all of the little girls aspiring to become physicians?

We understand that it can feel overwhelming when you consider your part in changing healthcare for the better. How can one person affect change? Sounds impossible, right? But we believe that each of us can. What if we asked: How can one person change the *experience* of healthcare, starting now? What small thing can you do *today*? How can you change *your own* experience?

Before opening our hearts and sharing our personal struggles, we were not feeling hopeful about our long-term careers as women physicians. In fact, we were looking for ways out of our everyday practice of medicine. And yes, with our valuable medical degrees, impressive resumes, and world-class education, it's pretty simple to jump ship and do something else. So why are we choosing to stay? Why are we choosing to bear these pains and stay in healthcare? Why are we choosing the harder path?

The reason is clear to us: we are choosing to be the Hope. That's right—Hope with a capital "H." And that means we are choosing to be the Change. That's right—Change with a capital "C." We are choosing to open our hearts and stay in Love, with a capital "L!"

Despite the pain, frustration, sacrifice, and hard work, we still understand and appreciate the tremendous privilege of being physicians. We recognize that, as flawed as our profession may be today, as crazy and as painful it is to work within today's healthcare system, and as toxic and dangerous our culture of medicine can be for practitioners, we are still the benefactors of the generations of women, scientists, researchers, professors—really, of all of humanity—who helped us to become the physicians we are today. It is with deep respect for the history of our profession, of medicine, of science, math, and technology, that we appreciate the privilege and honor of helping people through modern medicine.

Yes, being a physician today is not easy but, boy, it is still more necessary than ever. Because of the COVID-19 pandemic, we project a shortage of more than 139,000 physicians by 2033. That's a huge number! We recognize we'll be in our 50's by then, so who's going to take care of *us*? Who will we trust to care for our elderly parents, sick children, or neighbors-in-need?

As burned-out, bruised, battered, and stressed as we sometimes feel, women in healthcare must come together to resolve our modern-day corporate and systemic issues and to carry on the work of our forebearers in medicine. We strongly believe that we must not let our cynicism get the better of us. We must become the Hope. And yes, let us women in medicine lead this change. Who better than women to create this healthier, happier future in healthcare? The bottom line is that we love our families, our children, our patients, and our world too much to pass today's harsh medical culture to future generations, and so we choose to do what we can to change what we can.

As Tara Mohr describes, we are the "Transition Team."[53] We are the team of women who can choose to believe in a better, brighter, healthier future in medicine, even if we do not see the full results in our lifetimes. Even if we do not benefit today from our immediate efforts, we will still choose this path. Will our healthcare systems become our ideal workplace environments next month? Next year? Next decade? Probably not. Despite this, we are still willing to invest our time, energy, spirit, and heart toward this new, better reality.

And why not? What's the alternative?

Our strength in creating this change comes from our faith that this new path is possible, that change is possible, when we come together. Believing that together we can change our medical culture to become a kinder, more collaborative, more compassionate, more equal, more diverse, and more inclusive culture gives us hope. We are optimists to the core, and we know and believe that a world full of joy, and a better future for ourselves and others, is only possible if we journey together.

WILL YOU JOIN US ON THIS NEW PATH FORWARD?

IMAGINING THE 'FUTURE YOU'

We invite you now to close your eyes and imagine yourself ten years in the future.

Who are you?

Who do you want to be?

Our closing wish is for you to fall in love with the process of becoming the best version of yourself.

We are already grateful for the amazing woman you are! Connect with us anytime; we are here to support you on your journey to become your truest, most joyful, bold, and authentic self.

We love you, and we believe in you,

Luisa & Tammie

ACKNOWLEDGEMENTS

FROM LUISA

First and foremost, I would like to thank the love of my life, father of my children Michael. You are my "Marty Ginsburg," and it's with your daily love and friendship that I dream big, play big, and reach for the stars. Thank you, Annie, Peter, Ethan for reminding me what pure love and joy look like and how to play, laugh and have fun every day. Tremendous gratitude to my parents and brothers for teaching me how to love unconditionally, and have faith, hope and a strong work-ethic. Special thanks to several close and precious, loyal friends who have quietly inspired this work simply with their unconditional support and lifelong friendship—you all know who you are. I would like to acknowledge my professional career mentors—thank you for guiding and nurturing me under your powerful wings during my impressionable years as a young physician. Betsy Flanagan, your magical, compassionate approach helped me find my personal power during my lowest moments as a full-time practicing doctor, and for that I am forever grateful to you. Finally, my heartfelt thanks to my amazing women physician colleagues and my beautiful unicorn friend Tammie—know that by opening your hearts you have healed me, and I have no doubt, together we will change this world for the better.

FROM TAMMIE

I don't think it's possible to top Luisa's acknowledgements. I too, thank my husband Matthew, who is my "Marty," my life partner and team member. Living through the pandemic has brought me such clarity that I would never want to go through this with anyone else by my side. I love you and am grateful to you beyond words. My deep love and gratitude to my parents, Helen and Kuo, who taught me what true unconditional love is. My love to many precious friends from each phase of my life, you have taught me what true friendship is. And my gratitude to my teachers, mentors, coaches and colleagues, who have taught me the true meaning of service, and of living a life of deep purpose in the service of others. Lastly, to my beautiful friend Luisa, who saved me, and in creating Pink Coat, MD together, we have saved ourselves. Together, we will change our world for the better.

ABOUT THE AUTHORS

TAMMIE CHANG, MD

Dr. Tammie Chang is a board-certified physician in pediatric hematology/oncology practicing in Tacoma, Washington at Mary Bridge Children's Hospital. She is the Medical Director of the MultiCare Provider Wellness Program, Medical Director of Pediatric Infusion, and Founder and Director of her hospital's Pediatric Cancer Survivorship Program.

She earned her bachelor's degree and medical degree from Brown University and completed a four-year combined internal medicine and pediatrics residency at the University of Massachusetts. She completed her fellowship in pediatric hematology/oncology at St. Jude Children's Research Hospital, where she also served on staff as a solid tumor oncologist upon completing her fellowship training.

At a critical time in Tammie's career, she experienced debilitating burnout. She was exhausted in every way—emotionally, physically, mentally, and spiritually—while carrying immense pressure and was desperate for a way out. She sought help and solutions in order to survive and vowed to dedicate her life to supporting other women physicians to go beyond surviving to thriving.

Tammie is a certified empowerment and leadership coach for early career women physicians. She received her training from the Co-Active Training Institute and has additional training and certifications as a John Maxwell Leadership Coach, Trainer and Speaker; a Gallup CliftonStrengths Coach; and as a Tara Mohr Playing Big Facilitator.

Tammie currently lives in the Pacific Northwest with her husband, Matthew, and their four fur babies: Golden retrievers Gus and Toby, and cats Ellie and Mimi. Playing Rachmaninoff and Chopin on the piano and being active in the beautiful outdoors with her family are the favorite moments of her day!

LUISA DURAN, MD

Dr. Luisa Duran grew up in the San Francisco Bay Area, where today she loves practicing as a board-certified endocrinologist. A graduate from Brown University, where she earned her bachelor's and medical degree, she developed expertise in diabetes at the Joslin Diabetes Center with Harvard Medical School. She completed her internal medicine residency training at Santa Clara Valley Medical Center, an affiliate of Stanford University, and her fellowship in endocrinology, nutrition, and metabolism at the University of Washington in Seattle.

Luisa strongly believes that helping women physicians thrive in clinical practice creates a healthier, more equal, more joyful world! She understands the added challenges unique to women physicians, given her decade of clinical experience in various high-pressure healthcare environments across the United States. Speaking nationally about clinical practice, she realized how many women physicians share the same challenges. Learning of a colleague's crisis following severe physician burnout AND hearing her young daughter say she wants to "become a physician" propelled Luisa to collaborate with industry experts to provide solutions and change the future of medicine for women.

Luisa is profoundly grateful for her supportive husband, family, and friends, and her three young children, who inspire her every day to make the world a better place!

YOU DID IT!!

We are grateful for the amazing woman you are! Connect with us anytime; we are here to support you on your journey to become your truest, most joyful, bold, and authentic self.

We love you, and we believe in you.

Tammie & Luisa

OUR PINK COAT MINIFESTO

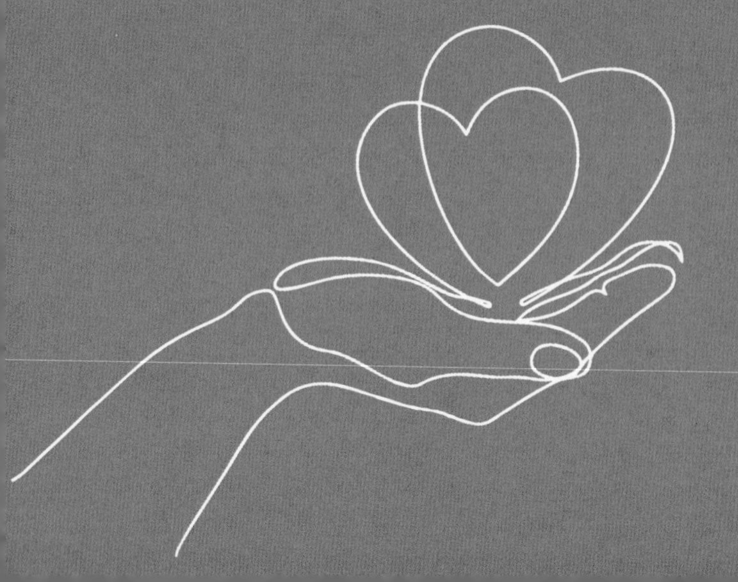

We are a **joyful, compassionate,** and **supportive** community of women physicians, dedicated to the personal and professional success and well-being of all women physicians.

We believe that medicine, and our world, **is a better place** when women doctors stay in medicine, lift each other up, and have a firm seat at the table.

We believe in **positivity**, over negativity.

We believe in **looking for solutions**, over problems.

We believe in **love**, over anger.

We believe in **joy**, over disappointment.

We believe in **speaking up for others**, over sitting in our silence.

We believe in **doing what is right**, over what is easy.

We believe in **lifting up** our fellow women in medicine, our sisters, and **backing each other up**.

We believe in **standing firm in our power**, and in our compassion.

We belive in not only taking a seat at the table, but *creating new seats for others*.

We are More than Enough –
We are Proud to Be Us!

FALL IN LOVE WITH THE PROCESS OF BECOMING THE BEST VERSION OF YOURSELF.

Tammie Chang, MD & Luisa Duran, MD

READY TO MAKE A CHANGE?

We have created a safe, loving commmunity for women physicians to come together and become their most joyful, compassionate, and bold selves. We invite you to join us as the amazing, wonderful, brilliant woman you are!!

JOIN OUR MEMBERSHIP HERE:

REFERENCES

1 Paturel, A. Why women leave medicine. *AAMC*, October 1, 2019. https://www.aamc.org/news-insights/why-women-leave-medicine

2 Mangurian, et al. What's holding women in medicine back from leadership. *Harvard Business Review*, Published June 19, 2018. Updated December 7, 2018. https://hbr.org/2018/06/whats-holding-women-in-medicine-back-from-leadership

3 West, et al. Physician burnout: contributors, consequences, solutions. *Journal of Internal Medicine*, 2018, 283; 516–52.

4 Hampton, T. Experts address risk of physician suicide. *JAMA*. 2005;294(10):1189-1191. doi:10.1001/jama.294.10.1189

5 Dutheil, et al. Suicide among physicians and health-care workers: A systemic review and meta-analysis. *PLOS One*, 2019.

6 Collier, R. Addressing physician burnout at the systems level. *CMAJ*, February, 2018.

7 West, C., et al. Resilience and burnout among physicians and the general US working population. *JAMA*, July, 2020.

8 West, et al. Physician burnout: contributors, consequences, solutions. *Journal of Internal Medicine*, 2018, 283; 516–52.

9 Schernhammer, E. S., & Colditz, G. A. Suicide rates among physicians: a quantitative and gender assessment (meta-analysis). *American Journal of Psychiatry AJP*, 161(12), 2295-2302, 2004.

10 Hampton, T. Experts address risk of physician suicide. *JAMA*. 2005;294(10):1189-1191. doi:10.1001/jama.294.10.1189

11 Fox, C., et al. The significant effect of diabetes duration on coronary heart disease mortality. *Diabetes Care*, March 2004; 27(3):704-8. doi: 10.2337/diacare.27.3.704.

12 Jagsi, R., et al. Sexual Harassment and discrimination experiences of academic medical faculty. *JAMA*, 315 (19): 2120-2121.

13 Mayo Clinic Staff. Job burnout: how to spot it and take action. *Mayo Clinic*. Updated June 5, 2021. https://www.mayoclinic.org/healthy-lifestyle/adult-health/in-depth/burnout/art-20046642

14 Paturel, A. Why women leave medicine. *AAMC*, October 1, 2019. https://www.aamc.org/news-insights/why-women-leave-medicine

15 Boyle, P., More women than men are enrolled in medical school. *AAMC*, December 9, 2019. https://www.aamc.org/news-insights/more-women-men-are-enrolled-medical-school

16 Mangurian, et al. What's holding women in medicine back from leadership. *Harvard Business Review*, Published June 19, 2018. Updated December 7, 2018. https://hbr.org/2018/06/whats-holding-women-in-medicine-back-from-leadership

17 Mangurian, et al. What's holding women in medicine back from leadership. *Harvard Business Review*, Published June 19, 2018. Updated December 7, 2018. https://hbr.org/2018/06/whats-holding-women-in-medicine-back-from-leadership

18 Kane, L. *Medscape Physician Compensation Report 2019*. Medscape, 2019.

19 Doximity. *2020 Physician Compensation Report. Fourth Annual Study*, Doximity, 2020.

20 Coury, et al. Women in the Workplace 2020, McKinsey & Company, September 30, 2020. https://www.mckinsey.com/featured-insights/diversity-and-inclusion/women-in-the-workplace

21 Coury, et al. Women in the Workplace 2020, McKinsey & Company, September 30, 2020. https://www.mckinsey.com/featured-insights/diversity-and-inclusion/women-in-the-workplace

22 Coury, et al. Women in the Workplace 2020, McKinsey & Company, September 30, 2020. https://www.mckinsey.com/featured-insights/diversity-and-inclusion/women-in-the-workplace

23 Fox, M. Men Have Been Promoted 3 Times More Than Women During the Pandemic, Study Finds. CNBC, October 13, 2020. https://www.cnbc.com/2020/10/13/pandemic-fallout-men-got-3-times-more-promotions-than-women.html

24 HIS Markit, Ltd. The Complexities of Physician Supply and Demand: Projections from 2018 to 2033. *AAMC*, June 2020. https://www.aamc.org/system/files/2020-06/stratcomm-aamc-physician-workforce-projections-june-2020.pdf

25 Han S, Shanafelt, T., et al. The business case for investing in physician well-being. *JAMA Intern Med*; 2017 Dec 1;177(12):1826-1832. doi: 10.1001/jamainternmed.2017.4340

26 Han S, Shanafelt, T., et al. The business case for investing in physician well-being. *JAMA Intern Med*; 2017 Dec 1;177(12):1826-1832. doi: 10.1001/jamainternmed.2017.4340

27 The Doctors Company TDC Group. *The Future of Health Care: A National Survey of Physicians 2018*. 2018. https://www.thedoctors.com/about-the-doctors-company/newsroom/the-future-of-healthcare-survey/

28 Dyrbye, L. et al. Effect of a professional coaching Intervention on the well-being and distress of physicians: a pilot randomized clinical trial. *JAMA Intern Med*; 2019 Oct 1;179(10):1406-1414. doi: 10.1001/jamainternmed.2019.2425.

29 Zenger J, Folkman, J. Research: Women are better leaders during a crisis. *Harvard Business Review*, December 30, 2020. https://hbr.org/2020/12/research-women-are-better-leaders-during-a-crisis

30 Garikipati et al. Leading the fight against the pandemic: does gender 'really' matter? *SSRN*, January 12, 2021. https://papers.ssrn.com/sol3/papers.cfm?abstract_id=3617953

31 Sergent K, Stajkovic, AD. Women's leadership is associated with fewer deaths during the COVID-19 crisis: quantitative and qualitative analyses of United States governors. *J Appl Psychology*; 2020 Aug; 105(8):771-783. doi: 10.1037/apl0000577. Epub 2020 Jul 2.

32 De Janasz, S and Cabrera, B. How women can get what they want in a negotiation. *Harvard Business Review*, August 17, 2018. https://hbr.org/2018/08/how-women-can-get-what-they-want-in-a-negotiation

33 Bean-Mellinger, B. The Average Length of Physicians' Careers. Chron.com, June 29, 2018. https://work.chron.com/average-length-doctors-careers-13376.html

34 De Janasz, S and Cabrera, B. How women can get what they want in a negotiation. *Harvard Business Review*, August 17, 2018. https://hbr.org/2018/08/how-women-can-get-what-they-want-in-a-negotiation

35 Babenko, O., et al. Association of physician's self-compassion with work engagement, exhaustion, and professional life satisfaction. *Med Sci* (Basel). 2019 Feb 12;7(2):29. doi: 10.3390/medsci7020029.

36 Wietmarschen, et al. Effects of mindfulness training on perceived stress, self-compassion, and self-reflection of primary care physicians: a mixed-method study. *BJGP Open*; 2018; 2(4); bjgpopen18X101621. DOI: https://doi.org/10.3399/bjgpopen18X101621

37 Juengst, S., et al. Family leave and return-to-work experience of physician mothers. *JAMA Netw Open*. 2019;2(10): e1913054. doi:10.1001/jamanetworkopen.2019.13054

38 Firth et al. AMA to promote use of peer support groups. Medpage Today, June 13, 2019. https://www.medpagetoday.com/meetingcoverage/ama/80467

39 Hu et al. Physicians' needs in coping with emotional stressors: the case for peer support. *Arch Surg*. 2012 Mar; 147(3):212-7. doi: 10.1001/archsurg.2011.312. Epub 2011 Nov 21.

40 Lane et al. Supporting clinicians after adverse events: development of a clinician peer support program. *J Patient Saf*; 2018 Sep; 14(3): e56-e60. doi: 10.1097/PTS.0000000000000508.

41 Wickham, J. Emotional exhaustion during times of unrest. Mayo Clinic, July 30, 2020. https://www.mayoclinichealthsystem.org/hometown-health/speaking-of-health/emotional-exhaustion-during-times-of-unrest

42 Houkes, I., et al. Development of burnout over time and the causal order of the three dimensions of burnout among male and female GPs: a three-wave panel study. *BMC Public Health*. 2011 Apr 18; 11:240. doi: 10.1186/1471-2458-11-240

43 Kane, L. Women Physicians 2020: The Issues They Care About. July 15, 2020. https://www.medscape.com/slideshow/2020-women-physicians-6013042

44 Galinsky, E. *Ask the Children: What America's Children Really Think About Working Parents*, New York, NY: William Morrow, 1999.

45 Miller, C. Mounting evidence of advantages for children of working mothers, *New York Times*, May 17, 2015.

46 Bologna, C. 13 Powerful quotes about motherhood from Shonda Rhimes. *Huffpost*, January 13, 2019. https://www.huffpost.com/entry/shonda-rhimes-motherhood-quotes_n_5c302bcce4b0d75a9830d167

47 Maslach C., et al. *Maslach Burnout Inventory Manual, 3rd ed.* Palo Alto, CA: Consulting Psychologists Press, 1996. Mayo Clinic Staff. Job burnout: how to spot it and take action. Mayo Clinic, Updated June 5, 2021. https://www.mayoclinic.org/healthy-lifestyle/adult-health/in-depth/burnout/art-20046642

48 Mayo Clinic Staff. Job burnout: how to spot it and take action. Mayo Clinic, Updated June 5, 2021. https://www.mayoclinic.org/healthy-lifestyle/adult-health/in-depth/burnout/art-20046642

49 Mayo Clinic Staff. Job burnout: how to spot it and take action. Mayo Clinic, Updated June 5, 2021. https://www.mayoclinic.org/healthy-lifestyle/adult-health/in-depth/burnout/art-20046642

50 Nagoski, A., Nagoski E. *Burnout: the secret to unlocking the stress cycle*. Random House Publishing Group, January 2020.

51 Neff, K. D. (2012). The science of self-compassion. In C. Germer & R. Siegel (Eds.), *Compassion and Wisdom in Psychotherapy* (pp. 79-92). New York, NY: Guilford Press.

52 Neff, K. D. (2012). The science of self-compassion. In C. Germer & R. Siegel (Eds.), *Compassion and Wisdom in Psychotherapy* (pp. 79-92). New York, NY: Guilford Press.

53 Mohr, T. (2015). *Playing Big: A practical guide for brilliant women like you*. Warwickshire, UK: Arrow Publishing Ltd. ASIN: B015HVMHLG

Made in United States
Orlando, FL
16 February 2022